Contents

Introduction

The Unit Assessment and the Benchmark Assessment are two distinct assessments designed to measure your students' mastery of specific skills. These tests include questions that cover the following areas:

Comprehension Strategies and Skills

Listening Comprehension

High-frequency Words

Phonemic Awareness (Unit Assessment only)

Phonics

Concept Words (Unit Assessment only)

When scheduling these assessments, you will need to decide whether to administer these in one or two sessions. These assessments are not intended to be timed, but for planning purposes, the Unit Assessment should take approximately forty minutes, and the Benchmark Assessment should take about the same amount of time.

In addition, we have included a brief **Print Awareness Assessment.** This will help you evaluate the student's readiness to read. It can be administered at any time of the year. There is also an Evaluation Form for recording your observations.

Unit Assessments assess how well students have mastered the skills taught in the unit. Benchmark Assessments are used for measuring progress over time. Both of these assessments will be explained in greater detail on the following pages.

How to Use the Unit Assessment

The Unit Assessment is given at the end of each unit. The assessment includes a fiction or a nonfiction listening passage, and questions focusing on the main skills taught throughout the unit.

Using the Results to Inform Instruction

Use the results of the Unit Assessment as a formative assessment tool to help monitor student progress. Information gathered by evaluating the results of this assessment can also be used to diagnose specific strengths and weaknesses of your students. If scores from the Unit Assessments are used to help determine report card grades, then you can consider this a summative assessment as well.

The scores from the Unit Assessment should be one of multiple measures used to help make instructional decisions for the coming unit. Analyze which skills students have mastered and which ones require further reteaching. This information, along with the results of other assessments and your own observations, can be used to determine grouping and instructional decisions. The unit charts in the back of this book will help you develop your reteaching plans.

How to Use the Benchmark Assessment

The Benchmark Assessment can be used to measure student progress throughout the year. There are two parallel forms of the test covering the same skills, and they are of equal difficulty. Administer Form A of the test at the beginning of the year and at the end of the year. Administer Form B of the test in the middle of the year.

The Benchmark Assessments align with the standards and objectives of standardized tests, most notably the TerraNova 2nd Edition and the National Assessment of Educational Progress (NAEP). They also align with the instructional design and skills built into the **Macmillan/McGraw-Hill Treasures** program.

Using the Results to Inform Instruction

The scores on the Benchmark Assessment should improve over time. The first Benchmark Assessment is administered in the fall, and scores are likely to be low as the items represent skills that may not have been taught yet. Scores on the assessment administered mid-year should show an overall increase, and the scores at the end of the year should be the most improved of all. If you compare or graph the results, scores should show an increase for each student. Students who do not show an improvement in scores should be further evaluated for additional support or the **Reading Triumphs** Intervention Program.

Administering the Assessments

The Unit Assessment consists of 22 to 27 multiple-choice questions. The format of the test varies depending on the skills taught in each unit. Each Benchmark Assessment consists of twenty-eight multiple-choice questions. The teacher script is provided with each Unit and Benchmark Assessment to help you explain each section of the test to students as you administer the test.

The **Answer Sheets** can be found on **pages 247–248.** There is one for the Unit Assessment and one for the Benchmark Assessment.

The **Answer Keys** to score the tests can be found on **pages 251–257.**

Directions: Say: *Write your name and the date on the cover of your test booklet.* (Or at the top of the Answer Sheet.) When all students are done, say: *Open the booklet to page 2.*

General Procedures

Before the test: Distribute copies of the assessment, and an Answer Sheet if you choose to use one.

During the test: Monitor students' test-taking behavior to make sure that each student is following the directions and writing responses in the correct places. Answer questions about procedures and materials, but do not help them answer the test questions.

After the test: Before collecting the papers, make sure that students have written their names on the cover of the test booklet or at the top of the Answer Sheet and any additional sheets of paper.

Listening Comprehension

Identify Setting

You are going to hear a story. After I read the story, I will ask you a few questions. Listen carefully. We will begin now.

The Playground

My mom and I are walking to the playground. When we get there, I'll swing on the swings and slide on the slide and climb on the playscape. Then we'll walk along the trail with the big trees. I hope we'll see a squirrel. I'll bet we'll stop at the ice cream stand and get two cones. If we do get ice cream, Mom will get vanilla and I'll get vanilla-and-chocolate swirl.

Turn to the first page with a picture of an alligator on it.

Check to see that all the children are on the correct page.

Point to the picture of the apple and the letter S.

Hold up page 3, pointing to the apple for the children to see.

I will read a question. Listen to the question as I read it aloud. In this story, what animal does the child hope to see on the trail? Look at the three pictures in this row. Choose the picture that shows the answer to the question and draw a circle around it. What is the answer?

Have a child provide the answer.

Yes, the second picture in the row shows a squirrel. The child hopes to see a squirrel when she walks along the trail with the big trees.

Check to see that each child has drawn a circle around the correct picture.

Does anyone have any questions?

Now I will read the story again. Listen carefully.

Read the story aloud again.

Now point to the picture of the star and the number 1.

Check to see that all the children are at the correct place.

Now I'm going to read another question. Listen to the question as I read it aloud: At the beginning of this story, where are the child and her mother going? Now look at the three pictures in this row. Choose the picture that shows the answer to the question and draw a circle around it.

Listening Comprehension

Make Predictions: High-Frequency Word

Turn to the page with a picture of a bee on it.

Check to see that all the children are on the correct page.

Point to the picture of the tree and the number 2.

Check to see that all the children are at the correct place.

Now I'm going to read another question. Listen to the question as I read it aloud: In this story, what will Mom and the child probably stop to get on the way home? Now look at the three pictures in this row. Choose the picture that shows the answer to the question and draw a circle around it.

Point to the picture of the apple and the number 3.

Check to see that all the children are at the correct place.

There are four words in this row. Find the word the in this row on your paper. Draw a circle around the word the on your paper.

Comprehension

Make Predictions

Turn to the page with a picture of a cat on it.

Check to see that all the children are on the correct page.

Point to the picture of the apple and the number 4.

Check to see that all the children are at the correct place.

Now look at the picture on the left. Draw a line from the picture on the left to the picture on the right that shows what will happen next.

Now point to the picture of the star and the number 5.

Check to see that all the children are at the correct place.

Now look at the picture on the left. Draw a line from the picture on the left to the picture on the right that shows what will happen next.

Comprehension
Identify Setting

Turn to the page with a picture of a dog on it.
Check to see that all the children are on the correct page.

Point to the picture of the apple and the number 6.
Check to see that all the children are at the correct place.

Look at the pictures in this row. Draw a circle around the one that shows where farm animals live.

Point to the picture of the star and the number 7.
Check to see that all the children are at the correct place.

Look at the pictures in this row. Draw a circle around the one that shows where you might go on a hot, sunny day.

High-Frequency Words
we, the

Turn to the page with a picture of an elephant on it.
Check to see that all the children are on the correct page.

Point to the picture of the apple and the letter S.
Check to see that all the children are at the correct place. Write the four words from row S on the board.

There are four words in this row. Find the word the in this row on your paper. Put your finger on it.
Have a child point to the word the on the chalkboard. Draw a circle around the word the on the chalkboard.

The word I circled is the word the. It is the word I asked you to find. Draw a circle around the word the on your paper.
Check to see that all the children have circled the correct word.

Does anyone have any questions?

We will continue in the same way. I will name some more words. Find the word I name in each row. Draw a circle around the word. Listen carefully.

Point to the picture of the star and the number 8.
Check to see that all the children are at the correct place.

Draw a circle around the word we.

Point to the picture of the tree and the number 9.
Check to see that all the children are at the correct place.

Draw a circle around the word the.

Phonemic Awareness
Onset and Rime Blending

Turn to the page with a picture of a frog on it.
Check to see that all the children are on the correct page.

Point to the picture of the apple and the letter S.
Check to see that all the children are at the correct place. Hold up page 8, pointing to the first row for all the children to see.

I will say a word in two parts. Listen carefully to its parts: /b/ /at/. Now I want you to put the parts together. Listen to these answer choices: bed, bat, cat. Which answer choice is a picture of the word that sounds like /b/ /at/? That's right, the word is bat. It is the same sound that is made with the two parts /b/ /at/. Draw a circle around the picture of the bat.
Check to see that all the children have circled the bat.

Does anyone have any questions?

Point to the picture of the star and the number 10.
Check to see that all the children are at the correct place.

Look at question 10. I will say a word in two parts. Listen carefully to its parts: /m/ /an/. Now I want you to put the parts together. Listen to these answer choices: man, pan, mop. Draw a circle around the picture that makes the sounds you hear in /m/ /an/.

Now point to the picture of the tree and the number 11.
Check to see that all the children are at the correct place.

Look at question 11. I will say a word in two parts. Listen carefully to its parts: /j/ /am/. Now I want you to put the parts together. Listen to these answer choices: pen, van, jam. Draw a circle around the picture that makes the sounds you hear in /j/ /am/.

Phonemic Awareness

Phoneme Isolation; Phoneme Blending

Turn to the page with a picture of a goat on it.

Check to see that all the children are on the correct page.

Point to the picture of the apple and the number 12.

Check to see that all the children are at the correct place.

Look at question 12. I will say a word: map, /m/ /a/ /p/. *What is the beginning sound in /m/ /a/ /p/? Listen to these answer choices:* bib, pig, moon. *Draw a circle around the picture that has the same beginning sound as /m/ /a/ /p/.*

Point to the picture of the star and the number 13.

Check to see that all the children are at the correct place.

Look at question 13. I will say a word in parts: /f/ /a/ /n/. What word do you make when you put these sounds together? Listen to these answer choices: net, fan, cap. *Draw a circle around the picture that has the same sounds as /f/ /a/ /n/.*

Phonics

Initial /m/m

Turn to the page with a picture of a horse on it.

Check to see that all the children are on the correct page.

Point to the picture of the apple and the letter S.

Check to see that all the children are at the correct place. Write the first letter from row S on the board followed by the four letter choices. Hold up page 10, pointing to the letter m in the box.

Look at the letter in the box. It is the letter m. *Look at the other four letters in this row.*

Have a child go to the board and point to the other occurrences of the letter m in the row. Draw a circle around each letter m on the board.

The letter I circled is the letter m. *Find the letter* m *in the box on your paper. Now find the letter* m *in the row of letters on your paper. Put your finger on it. Draw a circle around the letter* m. *Do you see the letter* m *anywhere else in the row? Put your finger on it. Draw a circle around the letter* m. *Do you see the letter* m *anywhere else in the row?*

Check to see that all the children have circled the two occurrences of the letter m.

Does anyone have any questions?

Point to the picture of the star and the number 14.

Check to see that all the children are at the correct place.

Say the name of the first picture that you see in this row. What beginning sound did you hear? Did you hear the /m/ sound in mouse? *Now write the letter* m *on the line.*

Check to see that each child wrote the letter m on the correct line.

Now say the names of the other pictures in this row. Draw a circle around the pictures whose names begin with the same sound as mouse.

Does anyone have any questions?

Point to the picture of the tree and the number 15.

Check to see that all the children are at the correct place.

Say the name of the first picture that you see in this row. What beginning sound did you hear? Did you hear the /m/ sound in mittens? *Write the letter* m *on the line. Now say the names of the other pictures in this row. Draw a circle around the pictures whose names begin with the same sound as* mittens.

Phonics

Final /m/m, Short /a/a

Turn to the page with a picture of a lizard on it.

Check to see that all the children are on the correct page.

We will continue on this page in the same way as the last page. Point to the picture of the apple and the number 16.

Check to see that all the children are at the correct place.

Say the name of the first picture that you see in this row. What sound did you hear at the end of the word? Did you hear the /m/ sound at the end of drum? *Write the letter* m *on the line. Now say the names of the other pictures in this row. Draw a circle around the pictures whose names end with the same sound as* drum.

Point to the picture of the star and the number 17.

Check to see that all the children are at the correct place.

Now we're going to listen for the middle sound. Say the name of the first picture that you see in this row. What sound did you hear in the middle of the word? Did you hear the /a/ sound in the middle of hat? Write the letter a on the line. Now say the names of the other pictures in this row. Draw a circle around the pictures whose names have the same middle sound as hat.

Phonics

Short /a/a

Turn to the page with a picture of a rabbit on it.

Check to see that all the children are on the correct page.

We will continue on this page in the same way as the last page. Point to the picture of the apple and the number 18.

Check to see that all the children are at the correct place.

Listen for the middle sound. Say the name of the first picture that you see in this row. What sound did you hear in the middle of the word? Did you hear the /a/ sound in the middle of hand? Write the letter a on the line. Now say the names of the other pictures in this row. Draw a circle around the pictures whose names have the same middle sound as hand.

Point to the picture of the star and the number 19.

Check to see that all the children are at the correct place.

Listen for the middle sound. Say the name of the first picture that you see in this row. What sound did you hear in the middle of the word? Did you hear the /a/ sound in the middle of mask? Write the letter a on the line. Now say the names of the other pictures in this row. Draw a circle around the pictures whose names have the same middle sound as mask.

Concept Words

big, small

Turn to the page with a picture of a kangaroo on it.

Check to see that all the children are on the correct page.

Point to the picture of the apple and the letter S.

Check to see that all the children are at the correct place.

Look at the pictures of the two dogs. One dog is big and one dog is small. Point to the dog that is big. That's right.

Check to see that all the children are pointing to the big dog.

Draw a circle around the dog that is big. Draw a line under the dog that is small.

Check to see that all the children circled the picture of the big dog and drew a line under the small dog.

Does anyone have any questions?

Now point to the picture of the star and the number 20. Look at the pictures of the two balls. Draw a circle around the ball that is big. Draw a line under the ball that is small.

Now point to the picture of the tree and the number 21. Look at the pictures of the two fire engines. Draw a circle around the fire engine that is big. Draw a line under the fire engine that is small.

Concept Words

short, tall

Turn to the next page, which has a picture of a lion on it.

Check to see that all the children are on the correct page.

Point to the picture of the apple and the number 22.

Check to see that all the children are at the correct place.

Look at the pictures of the two buildings. Make an X on the tall building. Draw a circle around the short building.

Now point to the picture of the star and the number 23.

Check to see that all the children are at the correct place.

Look at the pictures of the two trees. Make an X on the tall tree. Draw a circle around the short tree.

Name _____

Date _____

Treasures

Unit Assessment

TESTED SKILLS AND STRATEGIES

- **Listening Comprehension**
- **Comprehension**
- **High-Frequency Words**
- **Phonemic Awareness**
- **Phonics**
- **Concept Words**

Mc Graw Hill Macmillan McGraw-Hill

Name _____

S.

I.

2.

3.

my   the   we   that

4.

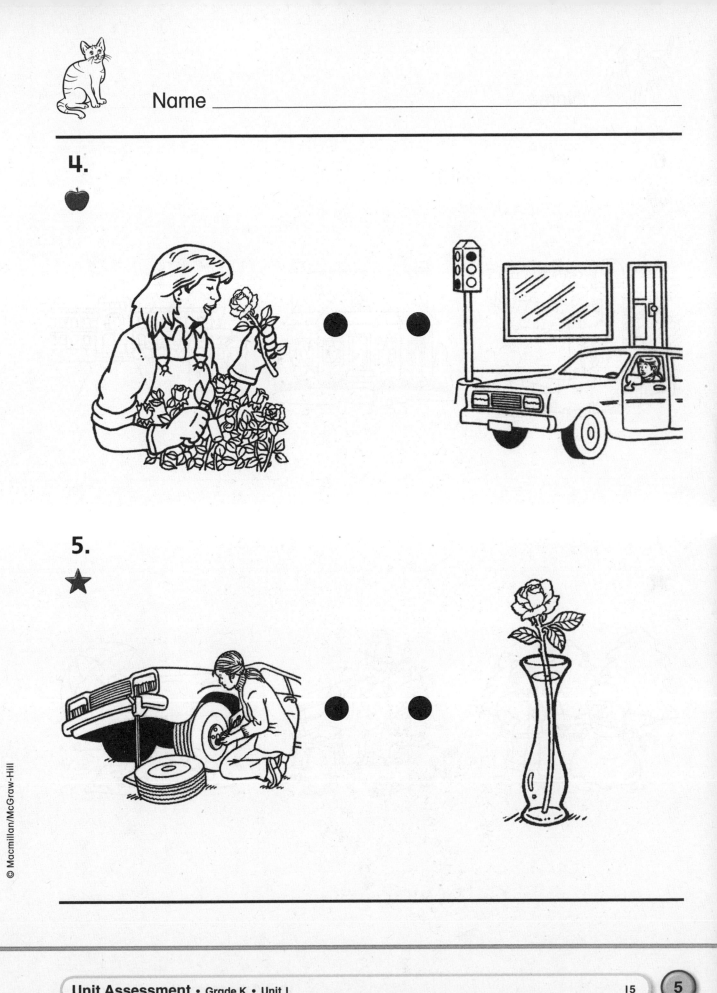

5.

6.

🍎

7.

★

Name _____

S.

🍎

that my the we

8.

★

the we that my

9.

🌲

we the my that

Name _____

9.

🍎

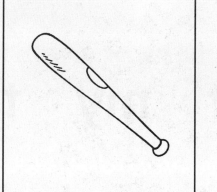 

10.

★

11.

🌲

Name _____

12.

13.

S.

🍎

m | m   n   m   r

14.

⭐

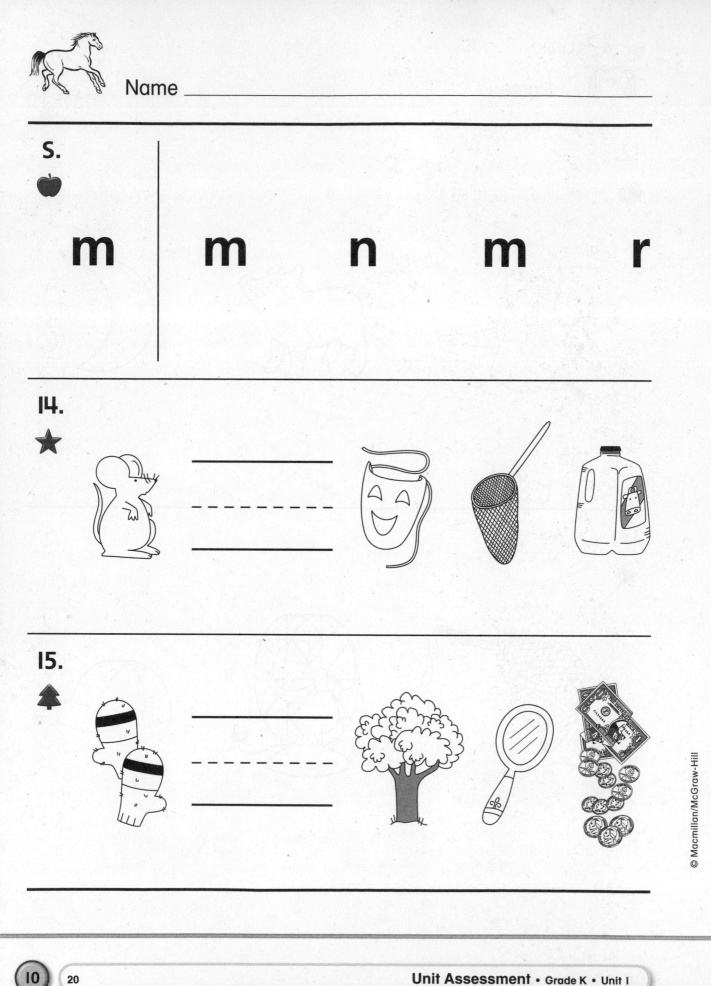

15.

🌲

16.

17.

18.

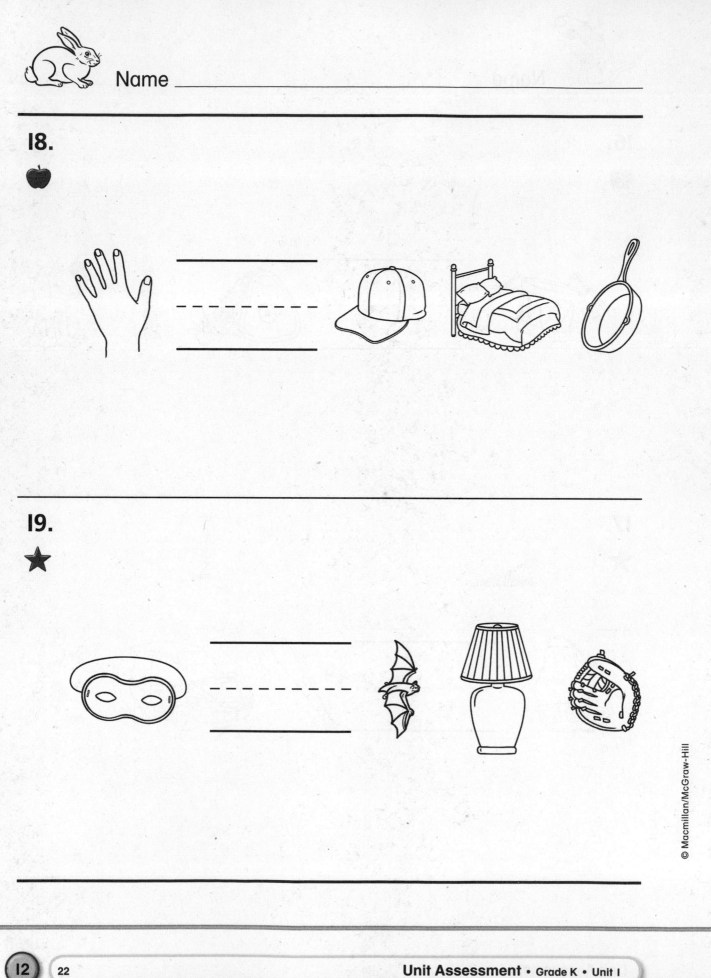

19.

S.

20.

21.

22.

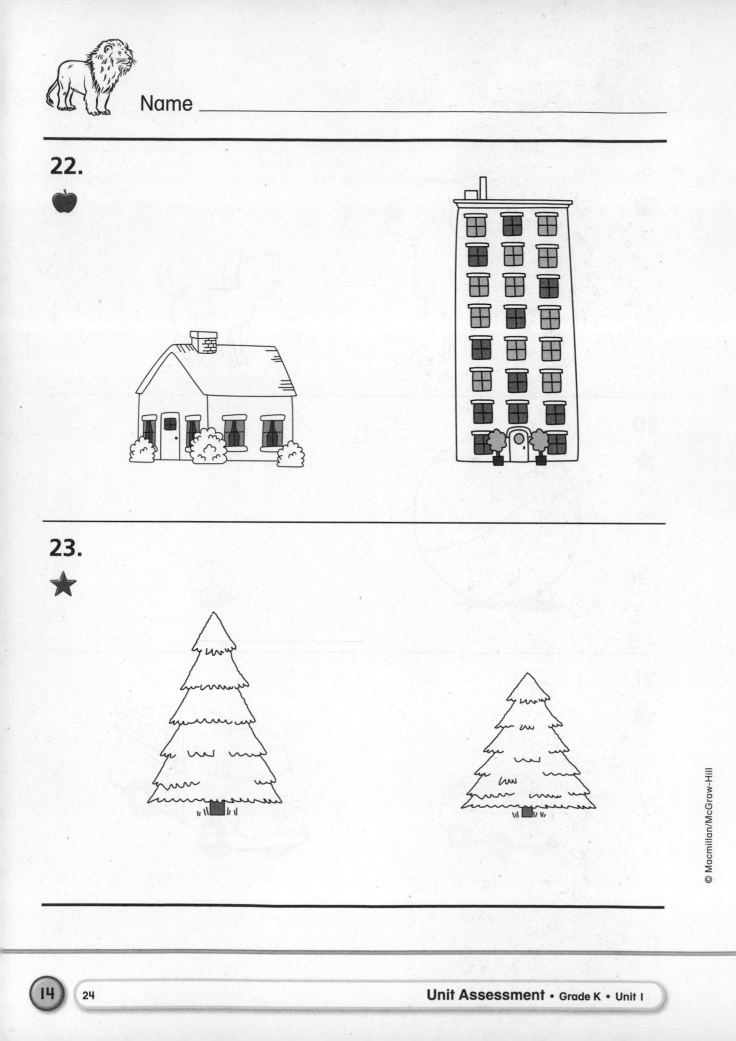

23.

Kindergarten • Unit 1

Student Evaluation Chart

TESTED SKILLS	Number Correct	Percent Correct
Listening Comprehension	/3	%
Identify setting, 1		
Make predictions, 2		
High-frequency word, 3		
Comprehension	/4	%
Make predictions, 4, 5		
Identify setting, 6, 7		
High-Frequency Words	/2	%
we, 9		
the, 8		
Phonemic Awareness	/4	%
Onset and rime blending, 10, 11		
Phoneme isolation, 12		
Phoneme blending, 13		
Phonics	/6	%
Initial and final /m/m, 14, 15, 16		
Short /a/a, 17, 18, 19		
Concept Words	/4	%
Size words: big/small, short/tall, 20, 21, 22, 23		
Total Unit Test Score	/23	%

Listening Comprehension

Identify Character

You are going to hear a story. After I read the story, I will ask you a few questions. Listen carefully. We will begin now.

A Trip to the Dentist

Leon was going to the dentist. He was getting his teeth cleaned. The dentist was very nice. She checked Leon's teeth and gums. "If we do not take care of our teeth, we will get cavities and need fillings," she said to Leon. "Be sure to brush your teeth every morning and every night." The dentist told Leon to use dental floss to clean between his teeth and help his gums. Leon got a good check-up!

Turn to the first page with a picture of an alligator on it.

Check to see that all the children are on the correct page.

Point to the picture of the apple and the letter S.

Hold up page 3, pointing to the apple for the children to see.

I will read a question. Listen to the question as I read it aloud. In this story, what is something that Leon should do every morning and every night? Look at the three pictures in this row. Choose the picture that shows the answer to the question and draw a circle around it. What is the answer?

Have a child provide the answer.

That's right, the third picture in the row shows a boy brushing his teeth. We should brush our teeth every morning and every night.

Check to see that each child has drawn a circle around the correct picture.

Does anyone have any questions?

Now I will read the story again. Listen carefully.

Read the story aloud again.

Now point to the picture of the star and the number 1.

Check to see that all the children are at the correct place.

Now I'm going to read another question. Listen to the question as I read it aloud: In this story, who checked Leon's teeth and gums? Now look at the three pictures in this row. Choose the picture that shows the answer to the question and draw a circle around it.

Listening Comprehension

High-Frequency Word

Turn to the page with a picture of a bee on it.

Check to see that all the children are on the correct page.

Point to the picture of the tree and the number 2.

Check to see that all the children are at the correct place.

There are four words in this row. Find the word <u>a</u> in this row on your paper. Draw a circle around the word <u>a</u> on your paper.

Comprehension

Compare and Contrast

Point to the picture of the apple and the number 3.

Check to see that all the children are at the correct place.

Look at the three pictures of bathroom sinks. Look at all the items on each sink. Which bathroom sink has the hairbrush? Draw a circle around the bathroom sink that has a hairbrush.

Comprehension

Identify Character

Turn to the page with a picture of a cat on it.

Check to see that all the children are on the correct page.

Point to the picture of the apple and the number 4.

Check to see that all the children are at the correct place.

Now look at the pictures in this row. Draw a circle around the picture of the king.

Now point to the picture of the star and the number 5.

Check to see that all the children are at the correct place.

Now look at the pictures in this row. Draw a circle around the picture of the sad face.

Comprehension

Compare and Contrast

Turn to the page with a picture of a dog on it.

Check to see that all the children are on the correct page.

Look at the two school boxes at the top of the page. Now look at the pictures along the left side of the page. Under each school box, put a check on the line if the school box has that item. Put an X on the line if the school box does not have that item.

High-Frequency Words

a, like

Turn to the page with a picture of an elephant on it.

Check to see that all the children are on the correct page.

Point to the picture of the apple and the letter S.

Check to see that all the children are at the correct place. Write the first word from row S on the board followed by the four word choices. Hold up page 7, pointing to the first word in the row so the children can see.

Look at the first word in the row. What is the word? That's right, the word is <u>we</u>. Look at the other four words in the row. I am going to draw a circle around the word where I see it in the same row.

Draw a circle around the second occurrence of the word <u>we</u> on the board.

The word I circled is the word <u>we</u>. It is the same as the first word in the row. Now you will do the same on your paper. Look at the first word in the apple row. Now draw a circle around the word where you see it in the same row.

Check to see that all the children have circled the one occurrence of the word <u>we</u> in the sample row.

Does anyone have any questions?

We will continue in the same way. Do the same thing for the next two rows. Look at the first word in each row. Then draw a circle around the word where you see it in the same row.

Phonemic Awareness

Phoneme Isolation

Turn to the page with a picture of a frog on it.

Check to see that all the children are on the correct page.

Point to the picture of the apple and the letter S.

Hold up page 8, pointing to the first row for all the children to see. Check to see that all the children are at the correct place.

I will say a word: <u>sun</u>, /s/ /u/ /n/. What is the beginning sound in /s/ /u/ /n/? Listen to these answer choices: <u>man</u>, <u>sled</u>, <u>cup</u>. Which picture has the same beginning sound as /s/ /u/ /n/?

Have a child provide the answer.

That's right. The second picture in the row is a <u>sled</u>. The word <u>sled</u> has the same beginning sound as the word <u>sun</u>. Draw a circle around the picture of the <u>sled</u> because it has the same beginning sound as the word <u>sun</u>.

Check to see that all the children have circled the picture of the <u>sled</u>.

Does anyone have any questions?

Now point to the picture of the star and the number 10.

Check to see that all the children are at the correct place.

Look at question 10. I will say a word: <u>sad</u>, /s/ /a/ /d/. What is the beginning sound in /s/ /a/ /d/? Listen to these answer choices: <u>hat</u>, <u>bed</u>, <u>seal</u>. Draw a circle around the picture that has the same beginning sound as /s/ /a/ /d/.

Now point to the picture of the tree and the number 11.

Check to see that all the children are at the correct place.

Look at question 11. I will say a word: <u>pin</u>, /p/ /i/ /n/. What is the beginning sound in /p/ /i/ /n/? Listen to these answer choices: <u>hen</u>, <u>pig</u>, <u>nest</u>. Draw a circle around the picture that has the same beginning sound as /p/ /i/ /n/.

Phonemic Awareness
Phoneme Blending

Turn to the page with a picture of a goat on it.
Check to see that all the children are on the correct page.

Point to the picture of the apple and the number 12.
Check to see that all the children are at the correct place.

Look at question 12. I will say a word in parts: /s/ /o/ /k/. What word do you make when you put these sounds together? Listen to these answer choices: <u>duck</u>, <u>sock</u>, <u>book</u>. *Draw a circle around the picture that has the same sounds as /s/ /o/ /k/.*

Now point to the picture of the star and the number 13.
Check to see that all the children are at the correct place.

Look at question 13. I will say a word in parts: /p/ /e/ /n/. What word do you make when you put these sounds together? Listen to these answer choices: <u>pen</u>, <u>pig</u>, <u>pot</u>. *Draw a circle around the picture that has the same sounds as /p/ /e/ /n/.*

Phonics
Initial /s/s

Turn to the page with a picture of a horse on it.
Check to see that all the children are on the correct page.

Point to the picture of the apple and the letter S.
Check to see that all the children are at the correct place.

Look at the picture of the <u>saw</u>. *Say* <u>saw</u>. *What beginning sound did you hear? Did you hear the /s/ sound in* <u>saw</u>? *Now write the letter* <u>s</u> *on the line.*
Check to see that all the children wrote the correct letter on the correct line.

We will continue in the same way on this page. Say the name of each picture. Then write the letter for the sound that you hear at the beginning of each picture name on the line.

Point to the picture of the star and the number 14.
Check to see that all the children are at the correct place.

Look at the picture of the <u>swing</u>. *Say* <u>swing</u>. *Write the letter for the sound that you hear at the beginning of the word* <u>swing</u>.

Point to the picture of the tree and the number 15.
Check to see that all the children are at the correct place.

Look at the picture of the <u>skates</u>. *Say* <u>skates</u>. *Write the letter for the sound that you hear at the beginning of the word* <u>skates</u>.

Phonics
Initial /p/p, Final /p/p

Turn to the page with a picture of a lizard on it.
Check to see that all the children are on the correct page.

Point to the picture of the apple and the number 16.
Check to see that all the children are at the correct place.

Look at the picture of the <u>pie</u>. *Say* <u>pie</u>. *Write the letter for the sound that you hear at the beginning of the word* <u>pie</u>.

Point to the picture of the star and the number 17.
Check to see that all the children are at the correct place.

Look at the picture of the <u>cap</u>. *Say* <u>cap</u>. *Write the letter for the sound that you hear at the end of the word* <u>cap</u>.

Does anyone have any questions?

Phonics
Review Initial /m/m, short /a/a

Turn to the page with a picture of a rabbit on it.
Check to see that all the children are on the correct page.

We will continue on this page in the same way as the last page.

Point to the picture of the apple and the number 18.
Check to see that all the children are at the correct place.

Look at the picture of the <u>moon</u>. *Say* <u>moon</u>. *Write the letter for the sound that you hear at the beginning of the word* <u>moon</u>.

Point to the picture of the star and the number 19.
Check to see that all the children are at the correct place.

Look at the picture of the <u>cat</u>. *Say* <u>cat</u>. *Write the letter for the sound that you hear in the middle of the word* <u>cat</u>.

Concept Words
Color: Red, Yellow

Turn to the page with a picture of a kangaroo on it.
Check to see that all the children are on the correct page.

Point to the picture of the apple and the letter S.
Check to see that all the children are at the correct place.

Look at the two pictures of buildings in this row. Color the firehouse red and the tall building blue. The first picture is a picture of a tall apartment building. Did you color it blue? That's right. The second picture is a picture of a firehouse. Did you color it red?
Check to see that all the children colored the apartment building blue and the firehouse red.

We will continue in the same way for the next two pictures.

Point to the picture of the star and the number 20. Look at the two pictures of fruit in this row. Color the apple red and the grapes yellow.

Concept Words
Colors: Red, Yellow, Blue

Turn to the next page, which has a picture of a lion on it.
Check to see that all the children are on the correct page.

Point to the picture of the apple and the number 21.
Check to see that all the children are at the correct place.

Look at the two pictures of vegetables in this row. Color the ear of corn yellow and the bunch of broccoli blue.

Now point to the picture of the star and the number 22.
Check to see that all the children are at the correct place.

Look at the two pictures of animals in this row. Color the dog blue and the turtle red.

Name _____

Date _____

Unit
Assessment
TESTED SKILLS AND STRATEGIES

- Listening Comprehension
- Comprehension
- High-Frequency Words
- Phonemic Awareness
- Phonics
- Concept Words

Macmillan
McGraw-Hill

Name _____

S.

I.

2.

🌲

we   the   a   like

3.

🍎

4.

5.

 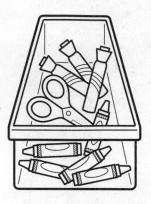

6.

7.

Name _____

S.

🍎

we | the   we   a   like

8.

★

a | we   and   my   a

9.

🌲

like | my   that   like   the

9.

10.

11.

Name _____

12.

13.

S.

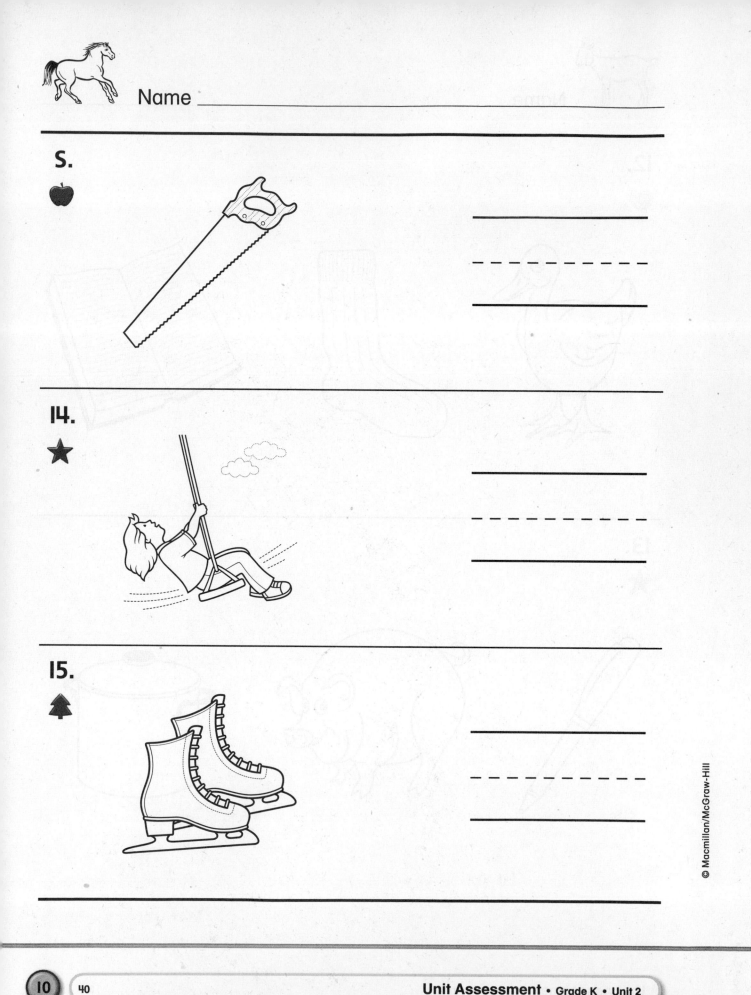

14.

15.

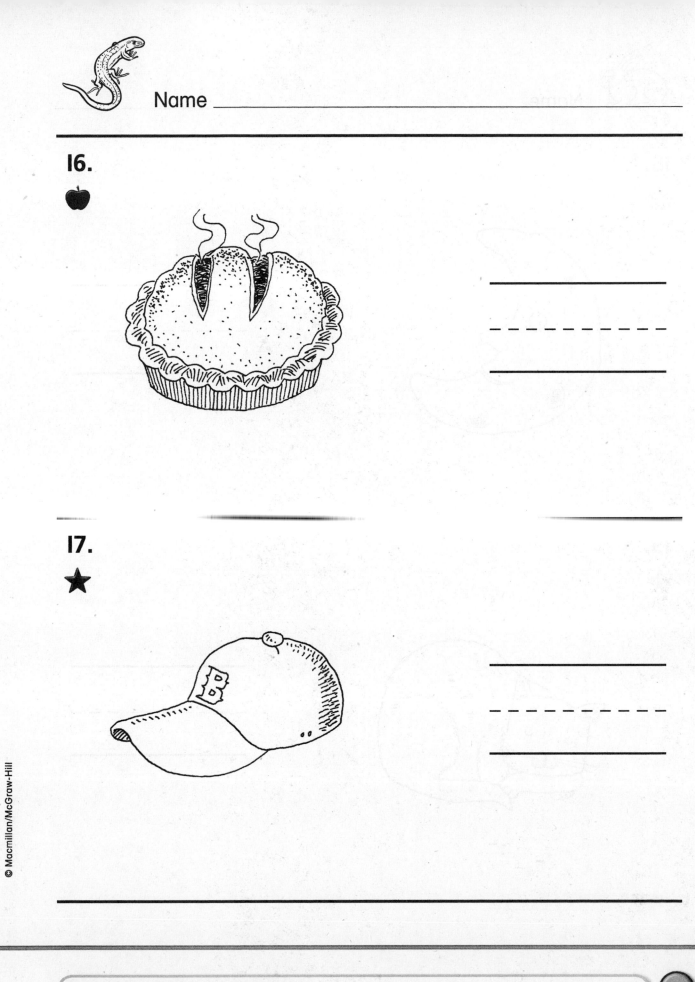

Name _____

16.

🍎

_____

- - - - - - - - - - - - - -

_____

17.

★

_____

- - - - - - - - - - - - - -

_____

18.

🍎

_____

- - - - - - - - - - - - - - - -

_____

19.

★

_____

- - - - - - - - - - - - - - - -

_____

Name _____

S.

20.

Name _____

21.

🍎

22.

★

© Macmillan/McGraw-Hill

Name _____

Student Evaluation Chart

TESTED SKILLS	Number Correct	Percent Correct
Listening Comprehension	/2	%
Identify character, 1		
High-frequency words, 2		
Comprehension	/5	%
Compare and contrast, 3, 6, 7		
Identify character, 4, 5		
High Frequency Words	/2	%
a, 8		
like, 9		
Phonemic Awareness	/4	%
Phoneme isolation, 10, 11		
Phoneme blending, 12, 13		
Phonics	/6	%
Initial /s/s, 14, 15		
Initial and final /p/p, 16, 17		
Review initial /m/m, 18		
Review short /a/a, 19		
Concept Words	/3	%
Color words: red, yellow, blue, 20, 21, 22		
Total Unit Test Score	/22	%

© Macmillan/McGraw-Hill

Listening Comprehension

Identify Character, Plot

You are going to hear a story. After I read the story, I will ask you a few questions. Listen carefully. We will begin now.

Bedtime

When it's time to go to bed, Tyler's mom asks him, "Which animal will you pretend to be tonight?" One night Tyler said, "A rabbit." His mom said, "Then let's see you hop, hop, hop to your toothbrush." After Tyler brushed his teeth, he gave his dog, Cody, a goodnight hug. In his bedroom, a storybook was waiting on his pillow. His mom read him a bedtime story and then kissed him goodnight.

Turn to the first page with a picture of an alligator on it.
Check to see that all the children are on the correct page.

Point to the picture of the apple and the letter S.
Hold up page 3, pointing to the apple for the children to see.

I will read a question. Listen to the question as I read it aloud: In this story, what was waiting on Tyler's pillow at bedtime? Look at the three pictures in this row. Choose the picture that shows the answer to the question and draw a circle around it. What is the answer?
Have a child provide the answer.

Yes, the second picture in the row shows what was waiting for Tyler. It is a picture of a storybook.
Check to see that each child has drawn a circle around the correct picture.

Does anyone have any questions?

Now I will read the story again. Listen carefully.
Read the story aloud again.

Now point to the picture of the star and the number 1.
Check to see that all the children are at the correct place.

Now I'm going to read another question. Listen to the question as I read it aloud: In this story, who helped Tyler get ready for bed? Now look at the three pictures in this row. Choose the picture that shows the answer to the question and draw a circle around it.

Listening Comprehension

High-Frequency Word

Turn to the page with a picture of a bee on it.
Check to see that all the children are on the correct page.

Point to the picture of the tree and the number 2.
Check to see that all the children are at the correct place.

There are four words in this row. Find the word go in this row on your paper. Draw a circle around the word go on your paper.

Comprehension

Classify and Categorize

Point to the picture of the apple and the number 3.
Check to see that all the children are at the correct place.

Now look at the pictures in this row. Draw a circle around the picture that does not belong.

Comprehension

Identify Character, Plot

Turn to the page with a picture of a cat on it.
Check to see that all the children are on the correct page.

Point to the picture of the apple and the number 4.
Check to see that all the children are at the correct place.

Look at each picture in this row. Each picture tells a story. Listen as I read a sentence that tells what one of the stories is about. Draw a circle around the picture that shows what the story is about.

Carmen is celebrating her sixth birthday. Draw a circle around the picture of Carmen.

Point to the picture of the star and the number 5.
Check to see that all the children are at the correct place.

Ming is helping his mother plant seeds in the garden. Draw a circle around the picture that tells this story.

Comprehension

Make and Confirm Predictions; Classify and Categorize

Turn to the page with a picture of a dog on it.

Check to see that all the children are on the correct page.

Point to the picture of the apple and the number 6.

Check to see that all the children are at the correct place.

Look at the picture on the left. Then look at the two pictures on the right. Circle the picture on the right that shows what will happen next.

Now point to the picture of the star and the number 7.

Check to see that all the children are at the correct place.

Now look at the pictures in this row. Draw a circle around the picture that does not belong.

High-Frequency Words

see, go

Turn to the page with a picture of an elephant on it.

Check to see that all the children are on the correct page.

Point to the picture of the apple and the letter S.

Check to see that all the children are at the correct place. Write the first word from row S on the board followed by the four word choices. Hold up page 7, pointing to the first word in the row so the children can see.

Look at the first word in the row. What is the word? That's right, the word is <u>like</u>. Look at the other four words in the row. I am going to draw a circle around the word where I see it in the same row.

Draw a circle around the second occurrence of the word <u>like</u> on the board.

The word I circled is the word <u>like</u>. It is same as the first word in the row. Now you will do the same on your paper. Look at the first word in the apple row. Now draw a circle around the word where you see it in the same row.

Check to see that all the children have circled the one occurrence of the word <u>like</u> in the sample row.

Does anyone have any questions?

We will continue in the same way. Do the same thing for the next two rows. Look at the first word in each row. Then draw a circle around the word where you see it in the same row.

Phonemic Awareness

Phoneme Isolation

Turn to the page with a picture of a frog on it.

Check to see that all the children are on the correct page.

Point to the picture of the apple and the letter S.

Hold up page 8, pointing to the first row for all the children to see. Check to see that all the children are at the correct place.

I will say a word: <u>tap</u>, /t/ /a/ /p/. What is the beginning sound in /t/ /a/ /p/? Listen to these answer choices: <u>pet</u>, <u>cap</u>, <u>tub</u>. Which answer choice has the same beginning sound as <u>tap</u>? That's right. The word <u>tub</u> has the same beginning sound as <u>tap</u>. Draw a circle around the picture of the <u>tub</u> because it has the same beginning sound as /t/ /a/ /p/.

Check to see that all the children have circled the picture of the <u>tub</u>.

Does anyone have any questions?

Now point to the picture of the star and the number 10.

Check to see that all the children are at the correct place.

Look at question 10. I will say a word: <u>toy</u>, /t/ /oy/. What is the beginning sound in /t/ /oy/? Listen to these answer choices: <u>top</u>, <u>boy</u>, <u>hat</u>. Draw a circle around the picture that has the same beginning sound as /t/ /oy/.

Now point to the picture of the tree and the number 11.

Check to see that all the children are at the correct place.

Look at question 11. I will say a word: <u>ten</u>, /t/ /e/ /n/. What is the beginning sound in /t/ /e/ /n/? Listen to these answer choices: <u>net</u>, <u>tail</u>, <u>pen</u>. Draw a circle around the picture that has the same beginning sound as /t/ /e/ /n/.

Name _____

S.

🍎

I.

★

Name _____

2.

🌲

we   the   a   like

3.

🍎

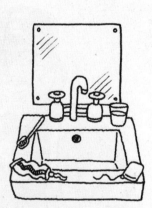 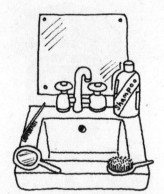 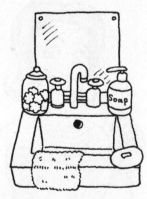

4.

🍎

5.

★

Name _____

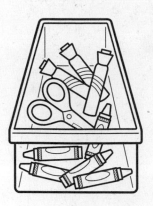

6.

🍎

GLUE

_____   _____

- - - - - - - - - - - -   - - - - - - - - - - - -

_____   _____

7.

★

_____   _____

- - - - - - - - - - - -   - - - - - - - - - - - -

_____   _____

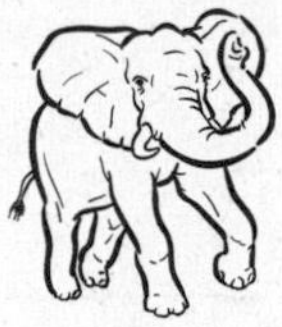

S.

🍎

| we | the | we | a | like |

8.

⭐

| a | we | and | my | a |

9.

🌲

| like | my | that | like | the |

Name _____

S.
🍎

10.
★

11.
🌲

Name _____

12.

13.

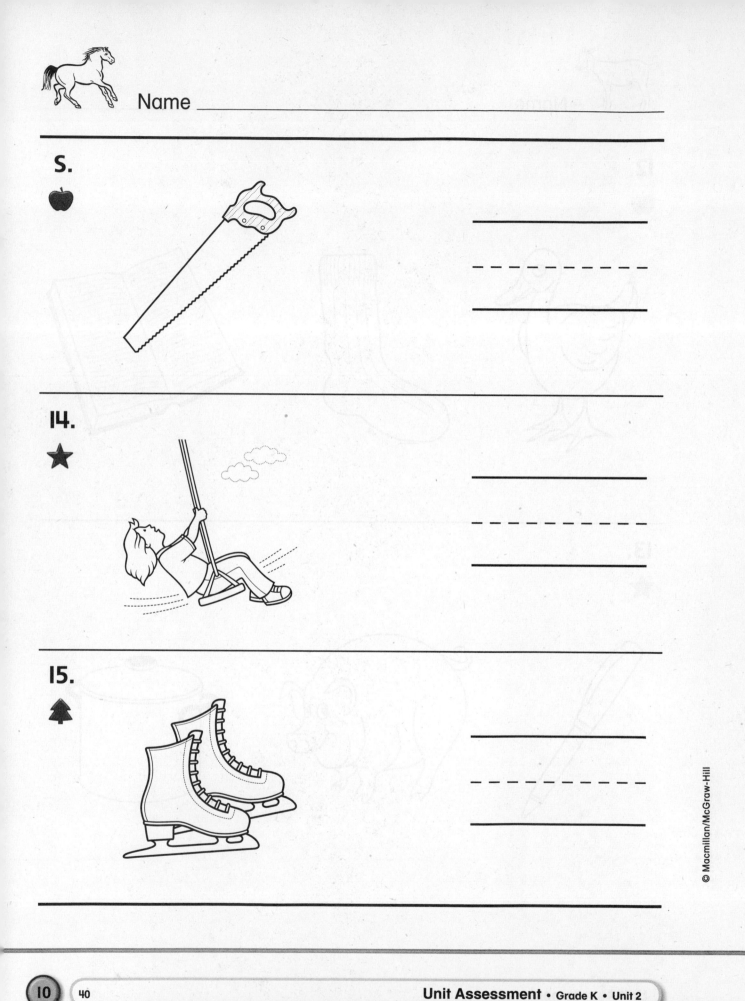

Name _____

S.

🍎

_____

– – – – – – – – – – – – – – – – –

_____

14.

★

_____

– – – – – – – – – – – – – – – – –

_____

15.

🌲

_____

– – – – – – – – – – – – – – – – –

_____

Unit Assessment • Grade K • Unit 2

16.

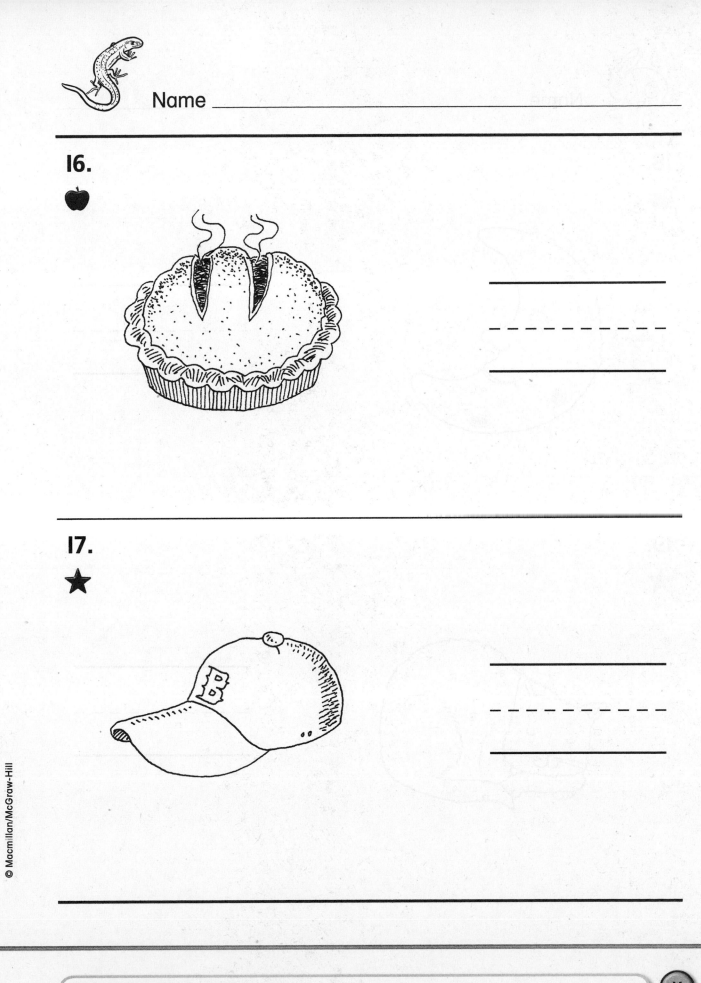

_____

- - - - - - - - - - - - -

_____

17.

★

_____

- - - - - - - - - - - - -

_____

18.

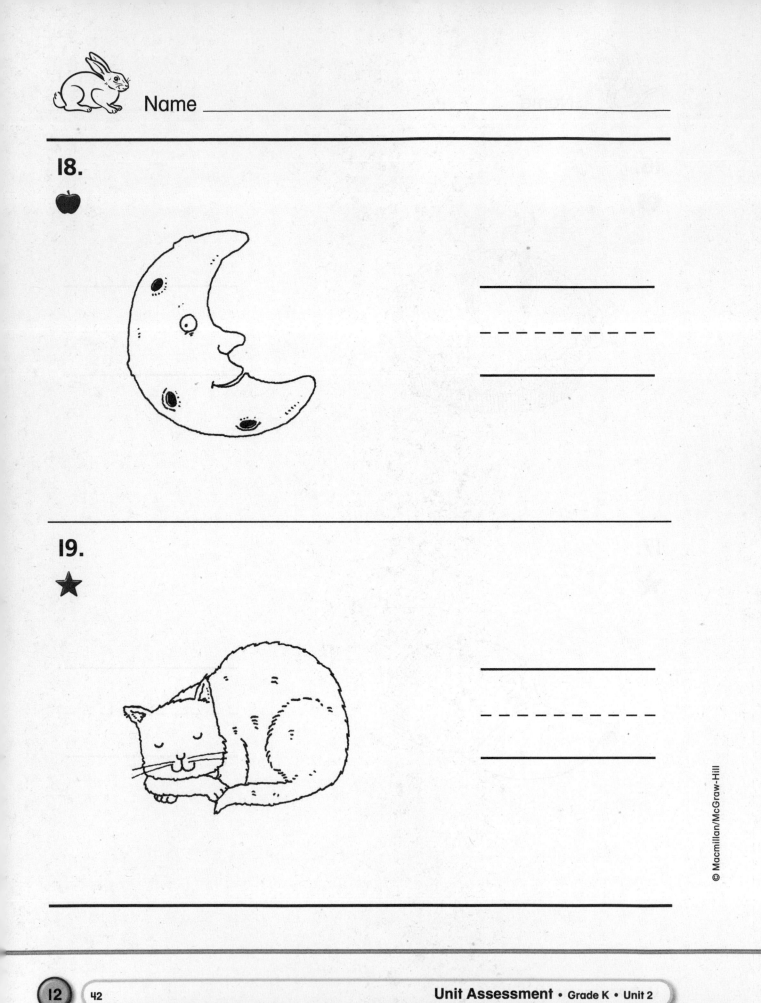

_____

\- \- \- \- \- \- \- \- \- \- \- \- \-

_____

19.

_____

\- \- \- \- \- \- \- \- \- \- \- \- \-

_____

Name _____

S.

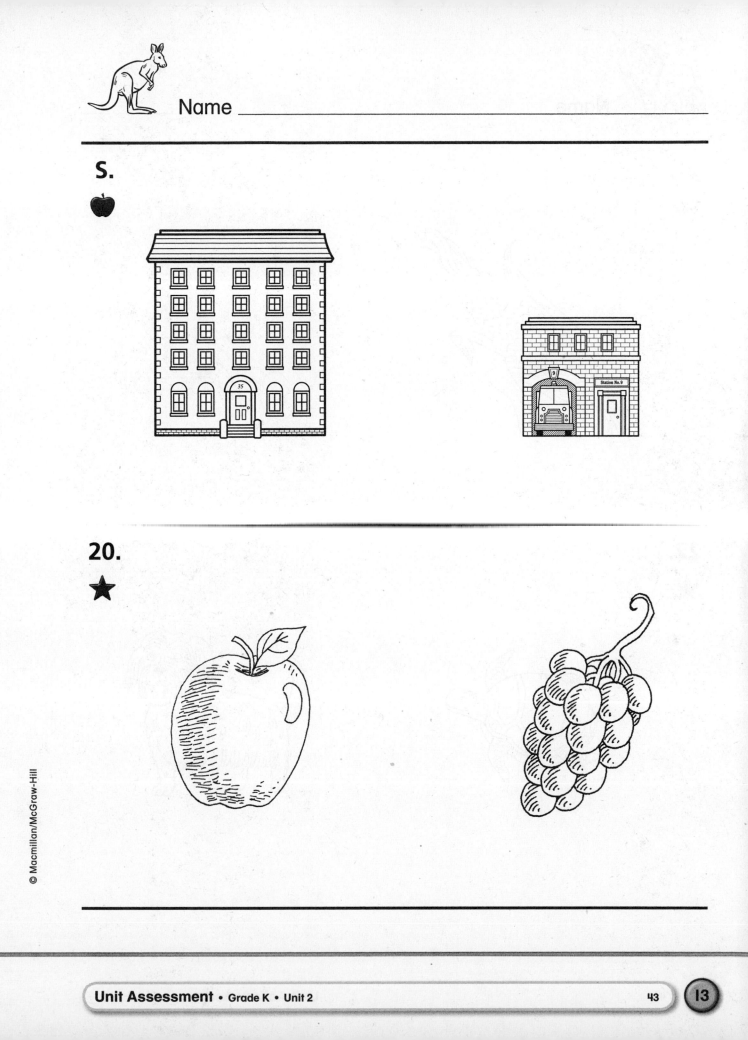

20.

Name _____

21.

🍎

22.

★

Kindergarten • Unit 2

Student Evaluation Chart

TESTED SKILLS	Number Correct	Percent Correct
Listening Comprehension	/2	%
Identify character, 1		
High-frequency words, 2		
Comprehension	/5	%
Compare and contrast, 3, 6, 7		
Identify character, 4, 5		
High Frequency Words	/2	%
a, 8		
like, 9		
Phonemic Awareness	/4	%
Phoneme isolation, 10, 11		
Phoneme blending, 12, 13		
Phonics	/6	%
Initial /s/s, 14, 15		
Initial and final /p/p, 16, 17		
Review initial /m/m, 18		
Review short /a/a, 19		
Concept Words	/3	%
Color words: red, yellow, blue, 20, 21, 22		
Total Unit Test Score	/22	%

© Macmillan/McGraw-Hill

Listening Comprehension

Identify Character, Plot

You are going to hear a story. After I read the story, I will ask you a few questions. Listen carefully. We will begin now.

Bedtime

When it's time to go to bed, Tyler's mom asks him, "Which animal will you pretend to be tonight?" One night Tyler said, "A rabbit." His mom said, "Then let's see you hop, hop, hop to your toothbrush." After Tyler brushed his teeth, he gave his dog, Cody, a goodnight hug. In his bedroom, a storybook was waiting on his pillow. His mom read him a bedtime story and then kissed him goodnight.

Turn to the first page with a picture of an alligator on it.

Check to see that all the children are on the correct page.

Point to the picture of the apple and the letter S.

Hold up page 3, pointing to the apple for the children to see.

I will read a question. Listen to the question as I read it aloud. In this story, what was waiting on Tyler's pillow at bedtime? Look at the three pictures in this row. Choose the picture that shows the answer to the question and draw a circle around it. What is the answer?

Have a child provide the answer.

Yes, the second picture in the row shows what was waiting for Tyler. It is a picture of a storybook.

Check to see that each child has drawn a circle around the correct picture.

Does anyone have any questions?

Now I will read the story again. Listen carefully.

Read the story aloud again.

Now point to the picture of the star and the number 1.

Check to see that all the children are at the correct place.

Now I'm going to read another question. Listen to the question as I read it aloud: In this story, who helped Tyler get ready for bed? Now look at the three pictures in this row. Choose the picture that shows the answer to the question and draw a circle around it.

Listening Comprehension

High-Frequency Word

Turn to the page with a picture of a bee on it.

Check to see that all the children are on the correct page.

Point to the picture of the tree and the number 2.

Check to see that all the children are at the correct place.

There are four words in this row. Find the word <u>go</u> in this row on your paper. Draw a circle around the word <u>go</u> on your paper.

Comprehension

Classify and Categorize

Point to the picture of the apple and the number 3.

Check to see that all the children are at the correct place.

Now look at the pictures in this row. Draw a circle around the picture that does not belong.

Comprehension

Identify Character, Plot

Turn to the page with a picture of a cat on it.

Check to see that all the children are on the correct page.

Point to the picture of the apple and the number 4.

Check to see that all the children are at the correct place.

Look at each picture in this row. Each picture tells a story. Listen as I read a sentence that tells what one of the stories is about. Draw a circle around the picture that shows what the story is about.

Carmen is celebrating her sixth birthday. Draw a circle around the picture of Carmen.

Point to the picture of the star and the number 5.

Check to see that all the children are at the correct place.

Ming is helping his mother plant seeds in the garden. Draw a circle around the picture that tells this story.

Comprehension

Make and Confirm Predictions; Classify and Categorize

Turn to the page with a picture of a dog on it.
Check to see that all the children are on the correct page.

Point to the picture of the apple and the number 6.
Check to see that all the children are at the correct place.

Look at the picture on the left. Then look at the two pictures on the right. Circle the picture on the right that shows what will happen next.

Now point to the picture of the star and the number 7.
Check to see that all the children are at the correct place.

Now look at the pictures in this row. Draw a circle around the picture that does not belong.

High-Frequency Words

see, go

Turn to the page with a picture of an elephant on it.
Check to see that all the children are on the correct page.

Point to the picture of the apple and the letter S.
Check to see that all the children are at the correct place. Write the first word from row S on the board followed by the four word choices. Hold up page 7, pointing to the first word in the row so the children can see.

Look at the first word in the row. What is the word? That's right, the word is <u>like</u>. *Look at the other four words in the row. I am going to draw a circle around the word where I see it in the same row.*
Draw a circle around the second occurrence of the word <u>like</u> **on the board.**

The word I circled is the word <u>like</u>. *It is same as the first word in the row. Now you will do the same on your paper. Look at the first word in the apple row. Now draw a circle around the word where you see it in the same row.*
Check to see that all the children have circled the one occurrence of the word <u>like</u> **in the sample row.**

Does anyone have any questions?

We will continue in the same way. Do the same thing for the next two rows. Look at the first word in each row. Then draw a circle around the word where you see it in the same row.

Phonemic Awareness

Phoneme Isolation

Turn to the page with a picture of a frog on it.
Check to see that all the children are on the correct page.

Point to the picture of the apple and the letter S.
Hold up page 8, pointing to the first row for all the children to see. Check to see that all the children are at the correct place.

I will say a word: <u>tap</u>, /t/ /a/ /p/. *What is the beginning sound in /t/ /a/ /p/? Listen to these answer choices:* <u>pet</u>, <u>cap</u>, <u>tub</u>. *Which answer choice has the same beginning sound as* <u>tap</u>? *That's right. The word* <u>tub</u> *has the same beginning sound as* <u>tap</u>. *Draw a circle around the picture of the* <u>tub</u> *because it has the same beginning sound as /t/ /a/ /p/.*
Check to see that all the children have circled the picture of the <u>tub</u>.

Does anyone have any questions?

Now point to the picture of the star and the number 10.
Check to see that all the children are at the correct place.

Look at question 10. I will say a word: <u>toy</u>, /t/ /oy/. *What is the beginning sound in /t/ /oy/? Listen to these answer choices:* <u>top</u>, <u>boy</u>, <u>hat</u>. *Draw a circle around the picture that has the same beginning sound as /t/ /oy/.*

Now point to the picture of the tree and the number 11.
Check to see that all the children are at the correct place.

Look at question 11. I will say a word: <u>ten</u>, /t/ /e/ /n/. *What is the beginning sound in /t/ /e/ /n/? Listen to these answer choices:* <u>net</u>, <u>tail</u>, <u>pen</u>. *Draw a circle around the picture that has the same beginning sound as /t/ /e/ /n/.*

Phonemic Awareness

Phoneme Blending

Turn to the page with a picture of a goat on it.

Check to see that all the children are on the correct page.

Point to the picture of the apple and the number 12.

Check to see that all the children are at the correct place.

Look at question 12. I will say a word in parts: /t/ /a/ /k/. What word do you make when you put these sounds together? Listen to these answer choices: tack, cat, duck. *Draw a circle around the picture that has the same sounds as /t/ /a/ /k/.*

Now point to the picture of the star and the number 13.

Check to see that all the children are at the correct place.

Look at question 13. I will say a word in parts: /k/ /i/ /k/. What word do you make when you put these sounds together? Listen to these answer choices: cap, kick, cup. *Draw a circle around the picture that has the same sounds as /k/ /i/ /k/.*

Phonics

Initial /t/t

Turn to the page with a picture of a horse on it.

Check to see that all the children are on the correct page.

Point to the picture of the apple and the letter S.

Check to see that all the children are at the correct place.

Hold up page 10, pointing to the first row for all the children to see.

Say the name of each picture. Which pictures have the same beginning sound as tip? *That's right,* tent *and* truck *have the same beginning sound as* tip. *They begin with the letter* t. *Draw a circle around the tent and the truck because they have the same beginning sound as* tip. *Now write the letter* t *on the line.*

Check to see that all the children circled the correct pictures and wrote the correct letter.

Does anyone have any questions?

We will continue in the same way on this page. Say the name of each picture. Draw a circle around each picture that has the same beginning sound as the word tip. *Then write the letter* t *on the line.*

Phonics

Final /t/t, Short /i/i

Turn to the page with a picture of a lizard on it.

Check to see that all the children are on the correct page.

Point to the picture of the apple and the number 16.

Check to see that all the children are at the correct place.

Now listen to the ending sound in the word hat. *Write the letter* t *on the line. Then say the name of each picture in this row. Which pictures have the same ending sound as* hat? *Draw a circle around the pictures that have the same ending sound as* hat.

Does anyone have any questions?

Phonics

Short /i/i

Point to the picture of the star and the number 17.

Check to see that all the children are at the correct place.

Now we're going to listen for the middle sound in the word sip. *Write the letter* i *on the line. Then say the name of each picture in this row. Which pictures have the same middle sound as* sip? *Draw a circle around the pictures that have the same middle sound as* sip.

Turn to the page with a picture of a rabbit on it.

Check to see that all the children are on the correct page.

Point to the picture of the apple and the number 18.

Check to see that all the children are at the correct place.

Say the name of the picture. Now read the two words next to the picture. Draw a circle around the word that names the picture. Now write the word that you circled on the line.

Check to see that all the children have circled and written the correct word.

Point to the picture of the star and the number 19.

Check to see that all the children are at the correct place.

Say the name of the picture. Now read the two words next to the picture. Draw a circle around the word that names the picture. Then write the word that you circled on the line.

Concept Words

Shape: Square

Turn to the page with a picture of a kangaroo on it.
Check to see that all the children are on the correct page.

Point to the picture of the apple and the letter S.
Check to see that all the children are at the correct place.

Look at the picture of the jack-in-the-box. Look at the three shapes next to the jack-in-the-box. Now we're going to find a shape in the jack-in-the-box that matches one of the shapes next to it. Which of the shapes next to the jack-in-the-box is the same as a shape in the jack-in-the-box? That's right. The square is the same as the shape in the jack-in-the-box. Now color the matching shapes blue.

Did you color both squares blue?
Check to see that all the children color both squares blue.

Does anyone have any questions?

Point to the picture of the star and the number 20.

We will continue in the same way. Look at the picture of a gift box. Now look at the three shapes next to it. Color the matching shapes yellow.

Concept Words

Shapes: Circle, Triangle

Turn to the next page, which has a picture of a lion on it.
Check to see that all the children are on the correct page.

Point to the picture of the apple and the number 21.
Check to see that all the children are at the correct place.

We will continue in the same way. Look at the picture of a girl holding a balloon. Now look at the three shapes next to it. Color the matching shapes red.

Now point to the picture of the star and the number 22.
Check to see that all the children are at the correct place.

Look at the picture of a teepee. Now look at the three shapes next to it. Color the matching shapes blue.

Name _____

Date _____

Unit
Assessment

TESTED SKILLS AND STRATEGIES

- Listening Comprehension
- Comprehension
- High-Frequency Words
- Phonemic Awareness
- Phonics
- Concept Words

Macmillan
McGraw-Hill

S.

🍎

I.

★

2.

🌲

we   the   like   go

3.

🍎

4.

5.

6.

7.

Name _____

S.

🍎

| like | see   we   like   go |

8.

★

| see | we   see   my   the |

9.

🌲

| go | a   the   go   see |

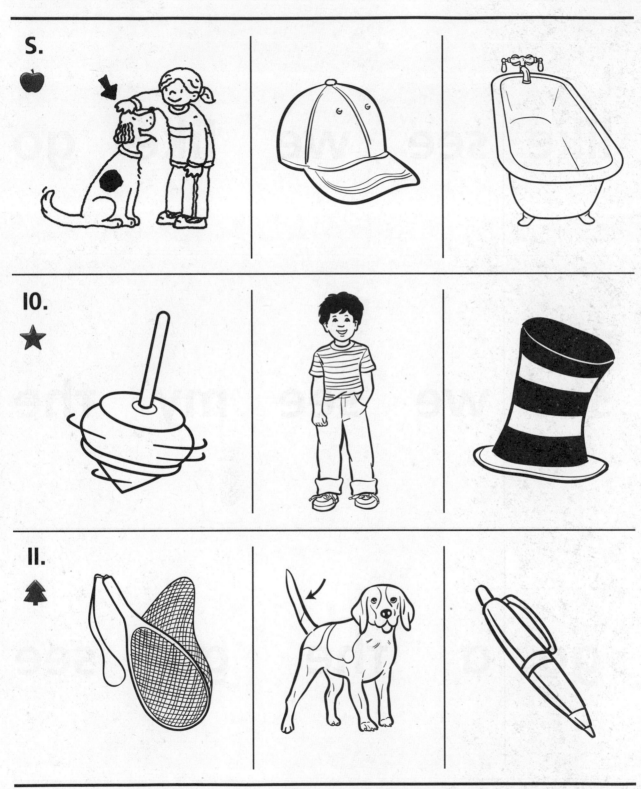

S.

10.

11.

12.

13.

Name _____

S.

14.

15.

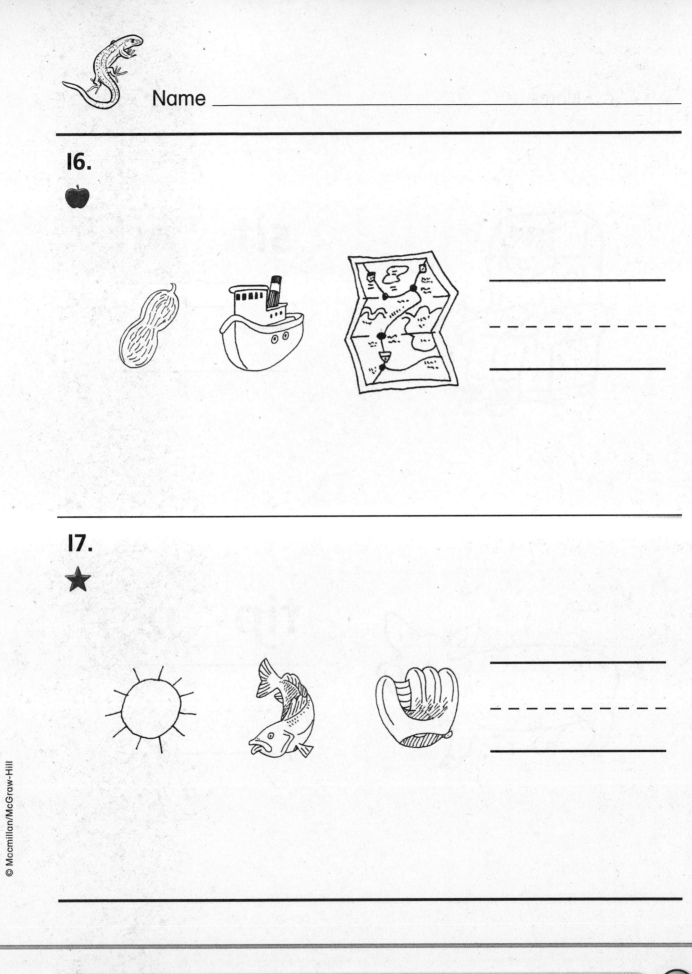

16.

17.

 Name _____

18.

sit pit

_____

- - - - - - - - - -

_____

19.

★

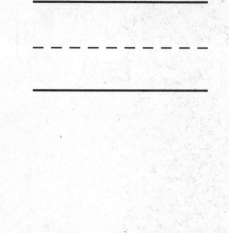

tip pig

_____

- - - - - - - - - -

_____

S.

20.

21.

22.

Name _____

Student Evaluation Chart

TESTED SKILLS	Number Correct	Percent Correct
Listening Comprehension	/2	%
Identify character, plot, 1		
High-frequency word, 2		
Comprehension	/5	%
Classify and categorize, 3, 7		
Identify character, plot, 4, 5		
Make and confirm predictions, 6		
High Frequency Words	/2	%
see, 8		
go, 9		
Phonemic Awareness	/4	%
Phoneme isolation, 10, 11		
Phoneme blending, 12, 13		
Phonics	/6	%
*Initial and final /t/*t, 14, 15, 16		
*Short /i/*i, 17, 18, 19		
Concept Words	/3	%
Shape words: square, circle, triangle, 20, 21, 22		
Total Unit Test Score	/22	%

Listening Comprehension

Identify Sequence of Events

You are going to hear a story. After I read the story, I will ask you a few questions. Listen carefully. We will begin now.

Ham and Cheese

Have you ever made a ham and cheese sandwich? You need two slices of bread and you need some ham and some cheese. First, you have to put the ham on one slice of bread. Next, put some cheese on the ham. Add mustard if you like it. Then, you could also put some lettuce on top. Finally, cover it with the other slice of bread. Ask a grown-up to cut the sandwich in half. Eat your sandwich and enjoy it!

Turn to page 3.

Check to see that all the children are on the correct page.

Point to the letter S.

Hold up page 3, pointing to the letter S for the children to see.

I will read a question. Listen to the narration as I read it aloud: In this story, why would you have to ask a grown-up for help? Now look at the three pictures in this row. Circle the picture that shows the answer to the question. What is the answer?

Have a child provide the answer.

That's right. The second picture in the row shows a grown-up cutting a sandwich in half.

Check to see that each child has drawn a circle around the correct picture.

Does anyone have any questions?

Now I will read the story again. Listen carefully.

Read the story aloud again.

Now point to number 1.

Check to see that all the children are at the correct place.

Now I'm going to read another question. Listen to the question as I read it aloud: In this story, just before you have to ask a grown-up for help, what is the last step in making a ham and cheese sandwich? Look at the three pictures in this row. Circle the picture that shows the answer to the question.

Listening Comprehension

High-Frequency Word

Turn to page 4.

Check to see that all the children are on the correct page.

Point to number 2.

Check to see that all the children are at the correct place.

There are four words in this row. Find the word <u>to</u> in this row on your paper. Draw a circle around the word <u>to</u> on your paper.

Comprehension

Make Inferences

Point to number 3.

Check to see that all the children are at the correct place.

Look at the pictures in number 3. What do you put water in? Look at the three pictures in this row. Circle the picture that shows the answer to the question.

Comprehension

Identify Sequence of Events

Turn to page 5.

Check to see that all the children are on the correct page.

Point to number 4.

Check to see that all the children are at the correct place.

Look at the three pictures in number 4. I am going to ask you to do something to each of the pictures. Listen carefully and look at the pictures. First, make an X on top of the picture that shows what happened first.

Now, draw a line under the picture that shows what happened next.

And now, draw a circle around the picture that shows what happened last.

Now point to number 5.

Check to see that all the children are at the correct place.

Look at the three pictures in number 5. I am going to ask you to do something to each of the pictures. Listen carefully and look at the pictures. First, make an X on top of the picture that shows what happened first.

Now, draw a line under the picture that shows what happened next.

And now, draw a circle around the picture that shows what happened last.

Comprehension

Make Inferences

Turn to page 6.

Check to see that all the children are on the correct page.

Point to number 6.

Check to see that all the children are at the correct place.

Look at the picture on the left. Then look at the two pictures on the right. Draw a line to the picture on the right that shows where the person is going.

Point to number 7.

Check to see that all the children are at the correct place.

Look at the picture on the left. Then look at the two pictures on the right. Draw a line to the picture on the right that shows where the person is going.

High-Frequency Words

to, have

Turn to page 7.

Check to see that all the children are on the correct page.

Point to the letter S.

Check to see that all the children are at the correct place. Write the first word from row S on the board followed by the four word choices. Hold up page 7, pointing to the first word in the row so the children can see.

Look at the first word in the row. What is the word? That's right, the word is see. Look at the other four words in the row. I am going to draw a circle around the word where I see it in the same row.

Draw a circle around the second occurrence of the word see on the board.

I circled the word see. It is the same as the first word in the row. Now you will do the same on your paper. Look at the first word in row S. Now draw a circle around the word where you see it in the same row.

Check to see that all the children have circled the second occurrence of the word see in row S.

Does anyone have any questions?

We will continue in the same way. Follow the same instructions for the next two rows. Look at the first word in each row. Then draw a circle around the word where you see it in the same row.

Phonemic Awareness

Phoneme Isolation

Turn to page 8.

Check to see that all the children are on the correct page.

Point to the letter S.

Hold up page 8, pointing to the first row for all the children to see. Check to see that all the children are at the correct place.

I will say a word: cat, /c/ /a/ /t/. What is the beginning sound in /c/ /a/ /t/? Listen to these answer choices: goat, car, bat. Which answer choice has the same beginning sound as cat? That's right. The word car has the same beginning sound as cat. Draw a circle around the picture of the car because it has the same beginning sound as the word cat.

Check to see that all the children have circled the picture of the car.

Does anyone have any questions?

Now point to number 10.

Check to see that all the children are at the correct place.

Look at question 10. I will say a word: nip, /n/ /i/ /p/. What is the beginning sound in /n/ /i/ /p/? Listen to these answer choices: nest, man, pin. Draw a circle around the picture that has the same beginning sound as /n/ /i/ /p/.

Now point to number 11.

Check to see that all the children are at the correct place.

Look at question 11. I will say a word: cold, /c/ /o/ /l/ /d/. What is the beginning sound in /c/ /o/ /l/ /d/? Listen to these answer choices: doll, lock, cup. Draw a circle around the picture that has the same beginning sound as /c/ /o/ /l/ /d/.

Phonemic Awareness

Phoneme Blending

Turn to page 9.

Check to see that all the children are on the correct page.

Point to number 12.

Check to see that all the children are at the correct place.

Look at question 12. I will say a word in parts: /n/ /e/ /k/. What word do you make when you put these sounds together? Listen to these answer choices: <u>net</u>, <u>neck</u>, <u>kiss</u>. *Draw a circle around the picture that has the same sounds as /n/ /e/ /k/.*

Now point to number 13.

Check to see that all the children are at the correct place.

Look at question 13. I will say a word in parts: /c/ /a/ /st/. What word do you make when you put these sounds together? Listen to these answer choices: <u>cast</u>, <u>cat</u>, <u>star</u>. *Draw a circle around the picture that has the same sounds as /c/ /a/ /st/.*

Phonics

Initial Letter /n/n

Turn to page 10.

Check to see that all the children are on the correct page.

Point to the picture at the top of the page.

Hold up page 10, pointing to the necklace at the top of the page.

What is the picture you see at the top of the page? That's right, it is a picture of a necklace. What sound do you hear at the beginning of the word <u>necklace</u>? *That's right, the /n/ sound. Write the letter* <u>n</u> *on the line.*

Point to the letter S in the first row.

Check to see that all the children are at the correct place.

Say the names of the three pictures in the row. Which pictures begin with the same sound as <u>necklace</u>? *That's right,* <u>nose</u> *and* <u>nap</u> *begin with the /n/ sound. Write the letter* <u>n</u> *on the line. Now circle the pictures of the nose and the nap because they have the same beginning sound as* <u>necklace</u>.

Check to see that all the children circled the correct pictures and wrote the correct letter.

Does anyone have any questions?

We will continue in the same way on this page for number 14 and number 15. Say the name of each picture. Write the letter <u>n</u> *on the line. Now draw a circle around each picture that has the same beginning sound as the word* <u>necklace</u>.

Phonics

Final /n/n

Turn to page 11.

Check to see that all the children are on the correct page.

Point to number 16.

Check to see that all the children are at the correct place.

Point to the picture at the top of the first box.

Hold up page 11, pointing to the van at the top of the page.

Now we're going to listen for the ending sound. Say the name of the picture you see at the top of the box. That's right, it is a picture of a van. What sound do you hear at the end of the word <u>van</u>? *That's right, the /n/ sound. Write the letter* <u>n</u> *on the line. Now say the word that names each picture at the bottom of the box. Which pictures have the same ending sound as* <u>van</u>? *Draw a circle around the pictures that have the same ending sound as* <u>van</u>.

Does anyone have any questions?

Point to number 17.

Check to see that all the children are at the correct place.

We will continue in the same way on this page for number 17. Point to the picture at the top of the second box. Listen for the ending sound. Say the name of the picture you see next to number 17. That's right, it is a picture of the sun. What sound do you hear at the end of the word <u>sun</u>? *That's right, the /n/ sound. Write the letter* <u>n</u> *on the line. Now say the word that names each picture at the bottom of the box. Which pictures have the same ending sound as* <u>sun</u>? *Draw a circle around the pictures that have the same ending sound as* <u>sun</u>.

Phonics
Initial /c/c

Turn to page 12.

Check to see that all the children are on the correct page.

Point to number 18.

Check to see that all the children are at the correct place.

Point to the picture at the top of the page.

Hold up page 12, pointing to the castle at the top of the page.

What is the picture you see at the top of the page? That's right, it is a picture of a castle. What sound do you hear at the beginning of the word castle? That's right, the /k/ sound. Write the letter c on the line.

Now say the word that names each picture at the bottom of the box. Which pictures have the same beginning sound as underline castle? Draw a circle around the pictures that have the same beginning sound as underline castle.

Does anyone have any questions?

Point to number 19.

Check to see that all the children are at the correct place.

We will continue in the same way on this page for number 19. Point to the picture at the top of the second box. Listen for the beginning sound. Say the name of the picture you see next to number 19. That's right, it is a camera. What sound do you hear at the beginning of the word camera? That's right, the /k/ sound. Write the letter c on the line. Now say the word that names each picture at the bottom of the box. Which pictures have the same beginning sound as underline camera? Draw a circle around the pictures that have the same beginning sound as underline camera.

Concept Words
Fruits and Vegetables: Apple

Turn to page 13.

Check to see that all the children are on the correct page.

Point to the letter S.

Check to see that all the children are at the correct place.

Look at the picture on the left. What is it? That's right, it's an apple. Is an apple a fruit or a vegetable? That's right, an apple is a fruit. Now look at the two pictures on the right. Does the apple belong in the bowl of fruit or does it belong on the plate of vegetables? I want you to draw a line from the apple to the picture on the right that shows where it belongs.

Did you draw a line from the apple to the bowl of fruit? Now color the apple green.

Check to see that all the children drew a line from the apple to the bowl of fruit and that they color the apple green.

Does anyone have any questions?

Point to number 20.

Check to see that all the children are at the correct place.

We will continue in the same way. Look at the next picture of a banana. Draw a line to the picture on the right that shows it is a fruit. Now color the banana yellow.

Concept Words
Fruits and Vegetables: Carrot, Banana

Turn to page 14.

Check to see that all the children are on the correct page.

Point to number 21.

Check to see that all the children are at the correct place.

We will continue in the same way. Look at the picture of a carrot. Draw a line to the picture on the right that shows it is a vegetable. Now color the carrot orange.

Now point to number 22.

Check to see that all the children are at the correct place.

Look at the picture of an apple. Draw a line to the picture on the right that shows it is a fruit. Now color the apple red.

Name _____

Date _____

Unit Assessment

TESTED SKILLS AND STRATEGIES

- Listening Comprehension
- Comprehension
- High-Frequency Words
- Phonemic Awareness
- Phonics
- Concept Words

Mc Graw Hill **Macmillan**
McGraw-Hill

S.

I.

2.

we   the   to   go

3.

4.

5.

6.

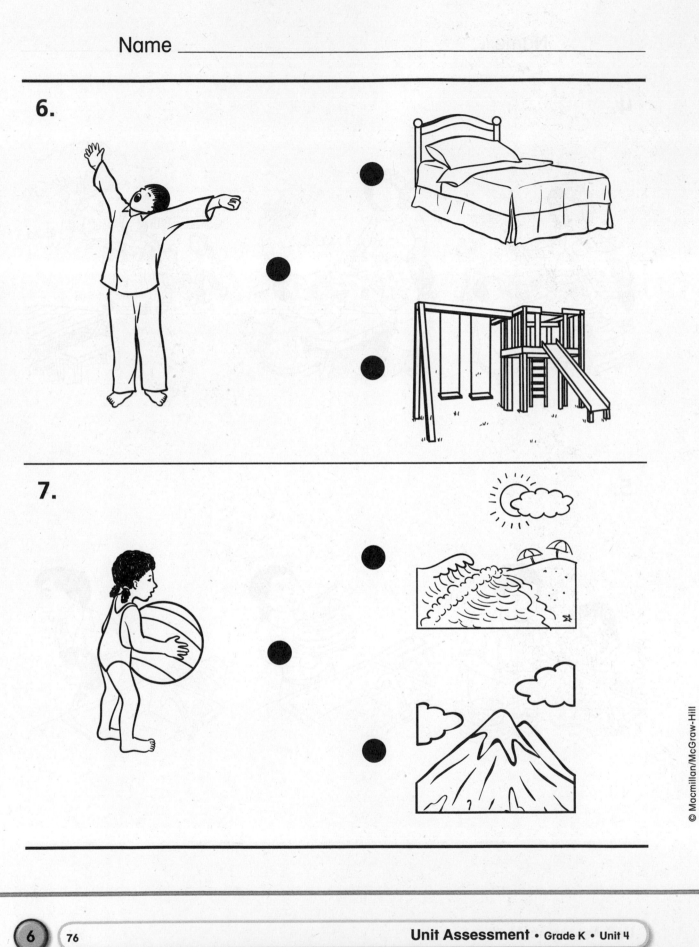

7.

Name ______________________________

S. see	see have to go
8. to	we the my to
9. have	like have the see

9.

10.

11.

12.

13.

Name _____

13.

14.

15.

Name _____

16.

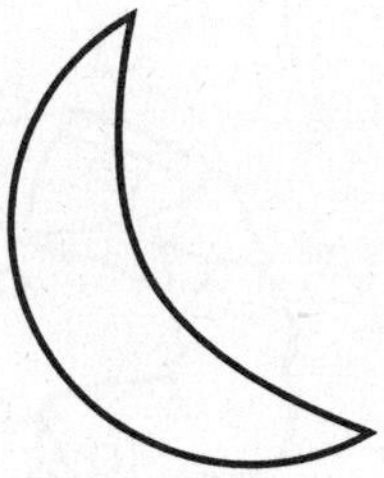

_____
- - - - - - - - - - - - - - -
_____

17.

_____
- - - - - - - - - - - - - - -
_____

18.  _____

- - - - - - - - - - - - - - - -

_____

19. _____

- - - - - - - - - - - - - - - -

_____

S.

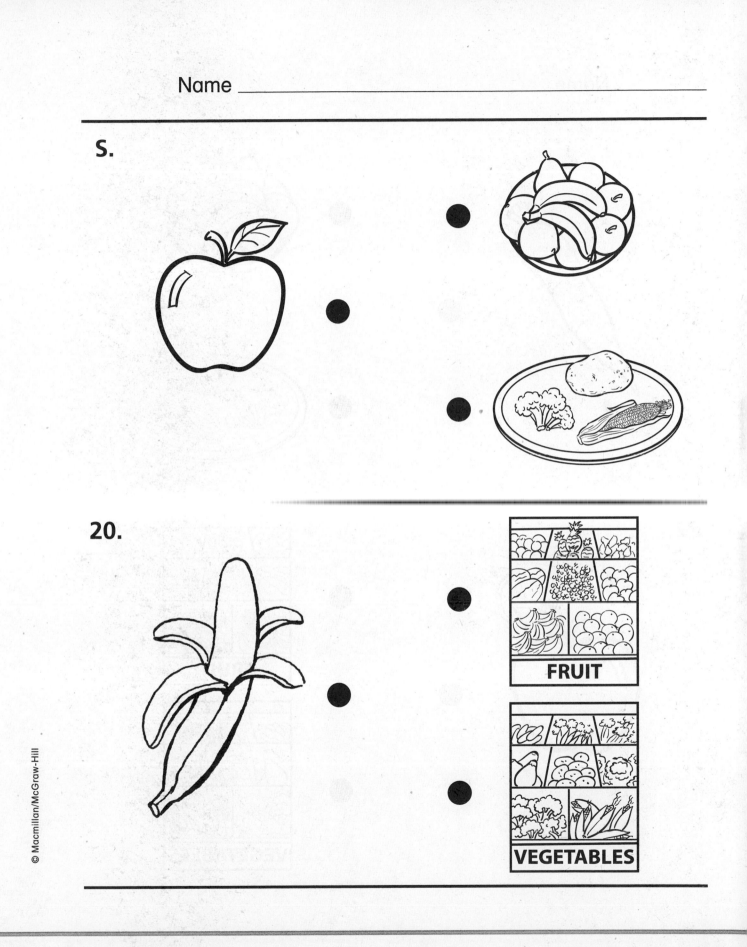

20.

21.

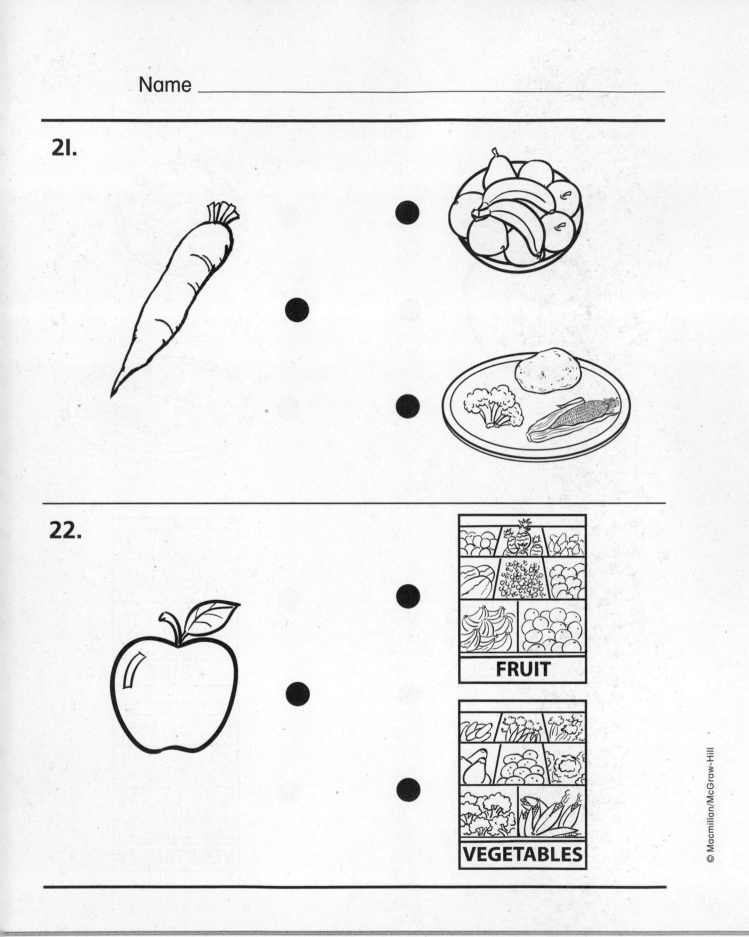

22.

FRUIT

VEGETABLES

Kindergarten • Unit 4

Student Evaluation Chart

TESTED SKILLS	Number Correct	Percent Correct
Listening Comprehension	/2	%
Identify sequence of events, 1		
High-frequency word, 2		
Comprehension	/5	%
Make inferences, 3, 6, 7		
Identify sequence of events, 4, 5		
High Frequency Words	/2	%
to, 8		
have, 9		
Phonemic Awareness	/4	%
Phoneme isolation, 10, 11		
Phoneme blending, 12, 13		
Phonics	/6	%
Initial and final /n/n, 14, 15, 16, 17		
Initial /c/c, 18, 19		
Concept Words	/3	%
Fruits and vegetables: apple, carrot, banana, 20, 21, 22		
Total Unit Test Score	/22	%

Listening Comprehension

Identify Character, Plot

You are going to hear a story. After I read the story, I will ask you a few questions. Listen carefully. We will begin now.

What Smells So Sweet?

Matthew is in the backyard. He is waiting for his brother to come out and play with him. He looks at the window and sees Victoria sitting tall on the windowsill. Her whiskers twitch as she smells the air. "I wonder what smells so sweet?" Victoria thinks. She holds her beautiful, bushy tail high as she walks along the windowsill. She lets out a soft meow. Matthew opens the door. Victoria leaps out to find the sweet smell of flowers all around her.

Turn to page 2.

Check to see that all the children are on the correct page.

Point to the letter S.

Hold up page 2, pointing to the letter S for the children to see.

I will read a question. Listen to the question as I read it aloud: In this story, whom will Matthew be playing with in the backyard? Now look at the three pictures in this row. Circle the picture that shows the answer to the question. What is the answer?

Have a child provide the answer.

That's right. The first picture in the row is a picture of Matthew's brother.

Check to see that each child has drawn a circle around the correct picture.

Does anyone have any questions?

Now I will read the story again. Listen carefully.

Read the story aloud again.

Now point to number 1.

Check to see that all the children are at the correct place.

Now I'm going to read another question. Listen to the question as I read it aloud: In this story, what does Victoria do when she goes outside? Look at the three pictures in this row. Circle the picture that shows the answer to the question.

Listening Comprehension

Make and Confirm Predictions; High-Frequency Words

Turn to page 3.

Check to see that all the children are on the correct page.

Point to number 2.

Check to see that all the children are at the correct place.

Listen to the question as I read it aloud: In this story, what do you think will happen when Matthew's brother goes outside? Look at the three pictures in this row. Circle the picture that shows the answer to the question.

Point to number 3.

Check to see that all the children are at the correct place.

There are four words in this row. Find the word is in this row on your paper. Draw a circle around the word is on your paper.

Comprehension

Identify Character, Plot

Turn to page 4

Check to see that all the children are on the correct page.

Point to number 4. Now look at the big picture.

Check to see that all the children are looking at the correct picture.

I am going to ask you to do something to the picture. Listen carefully and look at the picture. Anna and Brad are feeding the hamster. Draw a circle around Anna and Brad.

Now point to number 5. Look at the big picture.

Check to see that all the children are at the correct picture.

I am going to ask you to do something to the picture. Listen carefully and look at the picture. Crystal is watering the plant that is taller. Draw a circle around Crystal.

Comprehension

Classify and Catergorize, Make and Confirm Predictions

Turn to page 5.

Check to see that all the children are on the correct page.

Point to number 6.

Check to see that all the children are at the correct place.

Look at the pictures in this row. Draw a circle around the picture that does not belong.

Point to number 7.

Check to see that all the children are at the correct place.

Look at the picture on the left. Then look at the two pictures on the right. Draw a line to the picture on the right that shows what will happen next.

High-Frequency Words

is, play

Turn to page 6.

Check to see that all the children are on the correct page.

Point to the letter S.

Check to see that all the children are at the correct place. Write the first word from row S on the board followed by the four word choices. Hold up page 6, pointing to the first word in the row so the children can see.

Look at the first word in the row. What is the word? That's right, the word is have. *Look at the other four words in the row. I am going to draw a circle around the word where I see it in the same row.*

Draw a circle around the second occurrence of the word have **on the board.**

The word I circled is the word have. *It is the same as the first word in the row. Now you will do the same on your paper. Look at the first word in row S. Now draw a circle around the word where you see it in the same row.*

Check to see that all the children have circled the second occurrence of the word have **in row S.**

Does anyone have any questions?

We will continue in the same way. Follow the same instructions for the next two rows. Look at the first word in each row. Then draw a circle around the word where you see it in the same row.

Phonemic Awareness

Phoneme Isolation

Turn to page 7.

Check to see that all the children are on the correct page.

Point to the letter S.

Hold up page 7, pointing to the first row for all the children to see. Check to see that all the children are at the correct place.

I will say a word: fit, /f/ /i/ /t/. *What is the beginning sound in /f/ /i/ /t/? Listen to these answer choices:* fan, mitt, table. *Which answer choice has the same beginning sound as /f/ /i/ /t/? That's right. The word* fan *has the same beginning sound as* fit. *Draw a circle around the picture of the* fan *because it has the same beginning sound as /f/ /i/ /t/.*

Check to see that all the children have circled the picture of the fan.

Does anyone have any questions?

Now point to number 10.

Check to see that all the children are at the correct place.

Look at question 10. I will say a word: food, /f/ /ü/ /d/. *What is the beginning sound in /f/ /ü/ /d/? Listen to these answer choices:* doughnut, flower, moon. *Draw a circle around the picture that has the same beginning sound as /f/ /ü/ /d/.*

Now point to number 11.

Check to see that all the children are at the correct place.

Look at question 11. I will say a word: fat, /f/ /a/ /t/. *What is the beginning sound in /f/ /a/ /t/? Listen to these answer choices:* feet, hat, tiger. *Draw a circle around the picture that has the same beginning sound as /f/ /a/ /t/.*

Phonemic Awareness

Phoneme Blending

Turn to page 8.

Check to see that all the children are on the correct page.

Point to number 12.

Check to see that all the children are at the correct place.

*Look at question 12. I will say a word in parts:
/p/ /o/ /t/. What word do you make when you put these
sounds together? Listen to these answer choices:* <u>pen</u>,
<u>tent</u>, <u>pot</u>. *Draw a circle around the picture that has the
same sounds as /p/ /o/ /t/.*

Now point to number 13.

Check to see that all the children are at the correct place.

*Look at question 13. I will say a word in parts:
/f/ /i/ /sh/. What word do you make when you put these
sounds together? Listen to these answer choices:* <u>fist</u>,
<u>fish</u>, <u>ship</u>. *Draw a circle around the picture that has
the same sounds as /f/ /i/ /sh/.*

Phonemic Awareness

Phoneme Segmentation

Turn to page 9.

Check to see that all the children are on the correct page.

Point to number 14.

Check to see that all the children are at the correct place.

*Look at question 14. Listen while I say the sounds in the
word* <u>top</u>: */t/ /o/ /p/. How many sounds do you hear in the
word /t/ /o/ /p/? Say the word slowly. Circle the picture
that shows how many sounds you hear in /t/ /o/ /p/.*

Point to number 15.

Check to see that all the children are at the correct place.

*Look at question 15. Listen while I say the sounds in the
word* <u>fast</u>: */f/ /a/ /s/ /t/. How many sounds do you hear
in the word /f/ /a/ /s/ /t/? Say the word slowly. Circle the
picture that shows how many sounds you hear in
/f/ /a/ /s/ /t/.*

Phonics

Short /o/o

Turn to page 10.

Check to see that all the children are on the correct page.

Point to the letter S in the first row.

**Check to see that all the children are at the correct place.
Hold up page 10, pointing to the picture of the** <u>cot</u> **in the
first row.**

*Say the name of the picture. That's right, it is a picture
of a* <u>cot</u>. *Now read the two words next to the picture.
That's right, the first word is* <u>cat</u> *and the second word
is* <u>cot</u>. *Draw a circle around the word* <u>cot</u> *because it
names the picture. Now write the word that you circled
on the line. Did you write the word* <u>cot</u> *on the line?*

Check to see that all the children circled the word <u>cot</u> **and
wrote the word** <u>cot</u> **on the line.**

Does anyone have any questions?

*We will continue in the same way on this page for
number 16 and number 17. Say the name of the picture.
Then read the two words next to the picture. Draw a
circle around the word that names the picture. Then
write the word that you circled on the line.*

Phonics

Initial /f/f

Turn to page 11.

Check to see that all the children are on the correct page.

Point to number 18.

Check to see that all the children are at the correct place.

*We will continue in the same way on this page for
number 18 and number 19. Say the name of the picture.
Then read the two words next to the picture. Draw a
circle around the word that names the picture. Then
write the word that you circled on the line.*

Phonics

Short /o/o, Initial /f/f

Turn to page 12.

Check to see that all the children are on the correct page. Hold up page 12, pointing to the picture of the pot in the first row.

Point to number 20.

Check to see that all the children are at the correct place.

We will continue in the same way on this page for number 20 and number 21. Say the name of the picture. Then read the two words next to the picture. Draw a circle around the word that names the picture. Then write the word that you circled on the line.

Concept Words

Position Words: Behind, Under

Turn to page 13.

Check to see that all the children are on the correct page.

Point to the letter S.

Check to see that all the children are at the correct place.

Look at the picture. What do you see? That's right, it's a circus parade. Now we are going to look for the clown that is <u>behind</u> the elephant. Which clown is <u>behind</u> the elephant? That's right, the clown with striped pants is <u>behind</u> the elephant. Draw a circle around the clown that is <u>behind</u> the elephant.

Check to see that each child has drawn a circle around the clown with the striped pants.

Does anyone have any questions?

Point to number 22.

Check to see that all the children are at the correct place.

We will continue in the same way. Listen for the position words as you mark your page. Look at the picture. Draw a circle around the toys that are <u>under</u> the table.

Concept Words

Position Words: Behind, On

Turn to page 14.

Check to see that all the children are on the correct page.

Now look at the picture. I am going to ask you to do something to the picture. Listen carefully for the position words and look at the picture. First, make an X on the animals that are <u>behind</u> the fence. Now, draw a circle around the animals that are <u>on</u> the fence.

Name _____

Date _____

Unit
Assessment
TESTED SKILLS AND STRATEGIES

- **Listening Comprehension**
- **Comprehension**
- **High-Frequency Words**
- **Phonemic Awareness**
- **Phonics**
- **Concept Words**

Macmillan McGraw-Hill

S.

I.

2.

3.

see   is   to   go

4.

5.

Name _____

6.

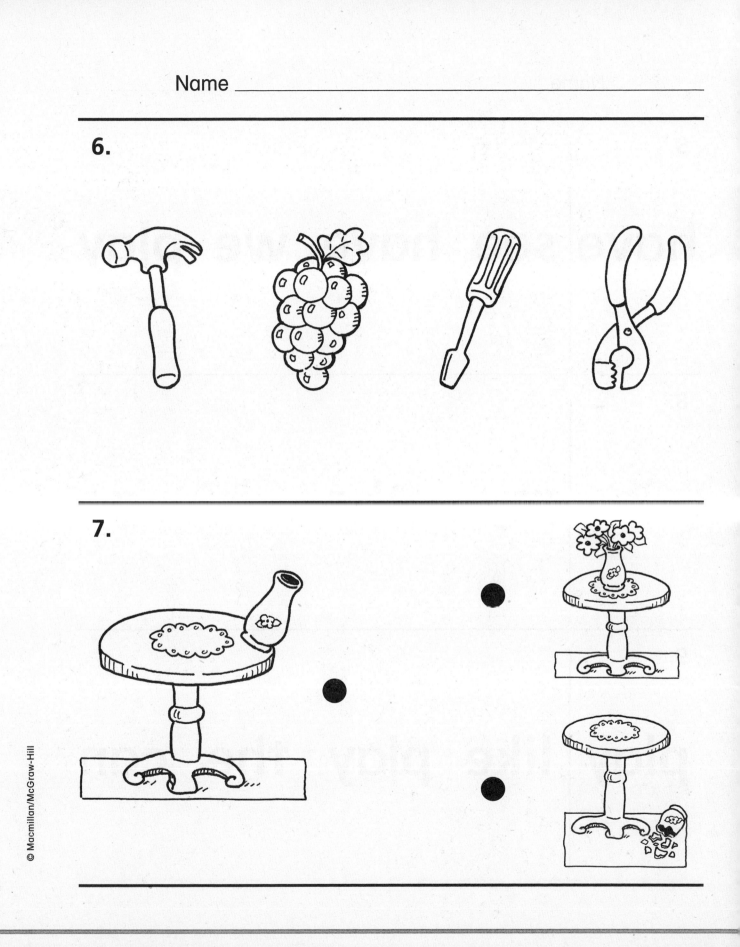

7.

Name ______________________________

S.	have	see	have	we	play
8.	is	my	the	is	go
9.	play	like	play	the	can

9.

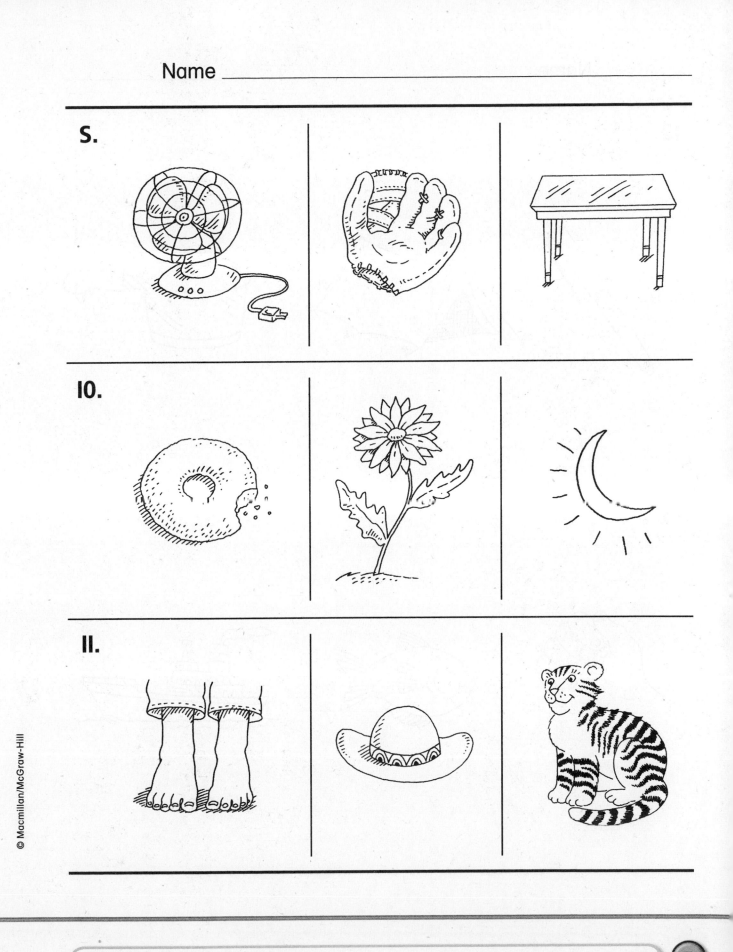

10.

11.

12.

13.

14.

15.

Name _____

S.

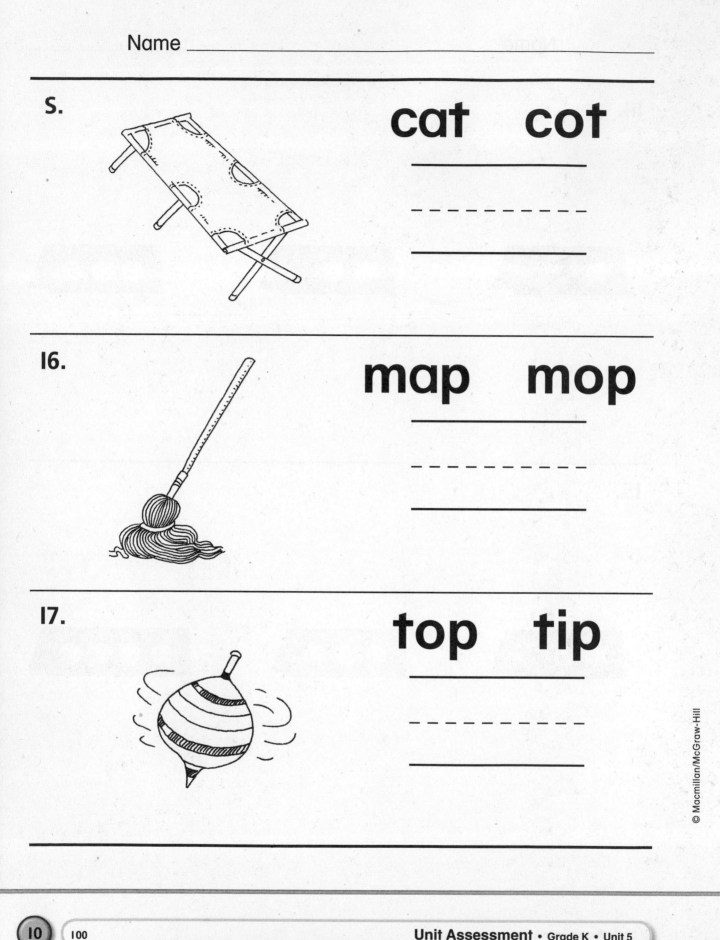

cat   cot

_____

- - - - - - - - - - - - - -

_____

16.

map   mop

_____

- - - - - - - - - - - - - -

_____

17.

top   tip

_____

- - - - - - - - - - - - - -

_____

© Macmillan/McGraw-Hill

Name _____

18.

fin   tin

_____

- - - - - - - - - - - - - - - - - -

_____

19.

pat   fan

_____

- - - - - - - - - - - - - - - - - -

_____

© Macmillan/McGraw-Hill

20.

pot   pat

_____

- - - - - - - - - - -

_____

21.

box   fox

_____

- - - - - - - - - - -

_____

S.

22.

23, 24.

Kindergarten • Unit 5

Student Evaluation Chart

TESTED SKILLS	Number Correct	Percent Correct
Listening Comprehension	/3	%
Identify character, plot, 1		
Make and confirm predictions, 2		
High-frequency word, 3		
Comprehension	/4	%
Identify character, plot, 4, 5		
Classify and categorize, 6		
Make and confirm predictions, 7		
High Frequency Words	/2	%
is, 8		
play, 9		
Phonemic Awareness	/6	%
Phoneme isolation, 10, 11		
Phoneme blending, 12, 13		
Phoneme segmentation, 14, 15		
Phonics	/6	%
Short /o/o, 16, 17, 20		
Initial /f/f, 18, 19, 21		
Concept Words	/3	%
Position words: under, behind, on, 22, 23, 24		
Total Unit Test Score	/24	%

Listening Comprehension
Identify Main Idea and Details

You are going to hear a story. After I read the story, I will ask you a few questions. Listen carefully. We will begin now.

The Five Senses

When you eat an apple, you are using your five senses. They are seeing, hearing, smelling, tasting, and touching. You use your eyes to see the apple. Your ears can hear the sound it makes when you bite off a piece. You use your nose to smell it and your mouth to taste it. And the whole time, you are using your hands to touch it. Next time you eat an apple, try to name the five senses that you are using!

Turn to page 2.

Check to see that all the children are on the correct page.

Point to the letter S.

Hold up page 2, pointing to the letter S for the children to see.

I will read a question. Listen to the question as I read it aloud: In this story, which part of your body do you use to smell the apple? Now look at the three pictures in this row. Fill in the circle under the right picture. What is the answer?

Have a child provide the answer.

That's right. The third picture in the row is a picture of a nose. You use your nose to smell the apple. You should have filled in the circle with a c inside.

Check to see that each child has filled in the correct circle.

Does anyone have any questions?

Now I will read the story again. Listen carefully.

Read the story aloud again.

Now point to number 1.

Check to see that all the children are at the correct place.

Now I'm going to read another question. Listen to the question as I read it aloud: In this story, which of your five senses will tell you if the apple is sweet? Look at the three pictures in this row. Fill in the circle under the picture that shows the answer to the question.

Listening Comprehension
High-Frequency Words

Turn to page 3.

Check to see that all the children are on the correct page.

Point to number 2.

Check to see that all the children are at the correct place.

Look at the first word in this row. Now look at the other three words in the row. Fill in the circle under the word that is the same as the first word in the row.

Reading Comprehension
Retell

Point to number 3.

Check to see that all the children are at the correct place.

Look at each picture. These pictures tell a story. Listen as I read three sentences. One sentence will tell what the story is about. Fill in the circle under the number of the sentence that tells what the story is about. Now listen carefully while I read the three sentences. Number 1: Jim and Pam play a game. Number 2: Jim and Pam pick apples for a pie. Number 3: Jim and Pam visit grandma's house.

Comprehension
Identify Main Idea and Details

Turn to page 4.

Check to see that all the children are on the correct page.

Point to number 4.

Check to see that all the children are at the correct place.

Look at the picture. Now read the sentences. Fill in the circle under the sentence that tells what the picture is all about.

Point to number 5.

Check to see that all the children are at the correct place.

Now do the same thing for this picture.

Comprehension

Retell

Turn to page 5.

Check to see that all the children are on the correct page.

Point to number 6.

Check to see that all the children are at the correct place.

Look at each picture. These pictures tell a story. Listen as I read three sentences. One sentence will tell what the story is about. Fill in the circle under the number of the sentence that tells what the story is about. Now listen carefully while I read the three sentences. Number 1: Sara gets ready for school. Number 2: Sara goes to the mall. Number 3: Sara goes to John's house.

Point to number 7.

Check to see that all the children are at the correct place.

Look at each picture. These pictures tell a story. Listen as I read three sentences. One sentence will tell what the story is about. Fill in the circle under the number of the sentence that tells what the story is about. Now listen carefully while I read the three sentences. Number 1: Pete plays with a friend. Number 2: Pete goes to school. Number 3: Pete plays with his toys.

High-Frequency Words

are, for, you

Turn to page 6.

Check to see that all the children are on the correct page.

Point to the letter S.

Check to see that all the children are at the correct place. Write the first word from row S on the board followed by the three word choices with their answer circles (a,b,c). Hold up page 7, pointing to the first word in the row so the children can see.

Look at the first word in the row. What is the word? That's right, the word is play. Look at the other three words in the row. I am going to fill in the circle under the word where I see it in the same row.

Fill in the circle c under the word play on the board.

The circle I filled in is c under the word play. It is the same as the first word in the row. Now you will do the same on your paper. Look at the first word in row S. Now fill in the circle under the word where you see it in the same row.

Check to see that all the children have filled in the circle c under the word play in row S.

Does anyone have any questions?

We will continue in the same way. Follow the same instructions for the next three rows. Look at the first word in each row. Then fill in the circle under the word where you see it in the same row.

Phonemic Awareness

Phoneme Isolation

Turn to page 7.

Check to see that all the children are on the correct page.

Point to the letter S.

Hold up page 7, pointing to the first row for all the children to see. Check to see that all the children are at the correct place.

I will say a word: dim, /d/ /i/ /m/. What is the beginning sound in /d/ /i/ /m/? Listen to these answer choices: map, Dad, fish. Which answer choice has the same beginning sound as /d/ /i/ /m/? That's right. Dad has the same beginning sound as /d/ /i/ /m/. Fill in the circle under the picture of Dad because it has the same beginning sound as the word /d/ /i/ /m/.

Check to see that all the children filled in the circle b under the picture of Dad.

Does anyone have any questions?

Now point to number 11.

Check to see that all the children are at the correct place.

Look at question 11. I will say a word: hop, /h/ /o/ /p/. What is the beginning sound in /h/ /o/ /p/? Listen to these answer choices: pot, horse, mop. Fill in the circle under the picture that has the same beginning sound as /h/ /o/ /p/.

Now point to number 12.

Check to see that all the children are at the correct place.

© Macmillan/McGraw-Hill

Look at question 12. I will say a word: rod, /r/ /o/ /d/. What is the beginning sound in /r/ /o/ /d/? Listen to these answer choices: door, frog, robot. Fill in the circle under the picture that has the same beginning sound as /r/ /o/ /d/.

Phonemic Awareness
Phoneme Blending

Turn to page 8.
Check to see that all the children are on the correct page.

Point to number 13.
Check to see that all the children are at the correct place.

Look at question 13. I will say a word in parts: /d/ /u/ /k/. What word do you make when you put these sounds together? Listen to these answer choices: cup, duck, book. Fill in the circle under the picture that has the same sounds as /d/ /u/ /k/.

Now point to number 14.
Check to see that all the children are at the correct place.

Look at question 14. I will say a word in parts: /r/ /a/ /m/. What word do you make when you put these sounds together? Listen to these answer choices: raft, ram, man. Fill in the circle under the picture that has the same sounds as /r/ /a/ /m/.

Phonemic Awareness
Phoneme Segmentation

Turn to page 9.
Check to see that all the children are on the correct page.

Point to number 15.
Check to see that all the children are at the correct place.

Look at question 15. Listen while I say the sounds in the word he: /h/ /ē/. How many sounds do you hear in the word /h/ /ē/? Say the word slowly. Fill in the circle under the picture that shows how many sounds you hear in /h/ /ē/.

Point to number 16.
Check to see that all the children are at the correct place.

Look at question 16. Listen while I say the sounds in the word dips: /d/ /i/ /p/ /s/. How many sounds do you hear in the word /d/ /i/ /p/ /s/? Say the word slowly. Fill in the circle under the picture that shows how many sounds you hear in /d/ /i/ /p/ /s/.

Point to number 17.
Check to see that all the children are at the correct place.

Look at question 17. Listen while I say the sounds in the word rat: /r/ /a/ /t/. How many sounds do you hear in the word /r/ /a/ /t/? Say the word slowly. Fill in the circle under the picture that shows how many sounds you hear in /r/ /a/ /t/.

Phonics
Initial /h/h, /d/d

Turn to page 10.
Check to see that all the children are on the correct page.

Point to the letter S in the first row.
Check to see that all the children are at the correct place. Hold up page 10, pointing to the picture of the house in the first row.

Say the name of the picture. That's right, it is a picture of a house. What beginning sound did you hear? Did you hear the /h/ sound in house? Fill in the circle under the letter h.
Check to see that each child filled in the correct circle.

Does anyone have any questions?

We will continue in the same way on this page for number 18 and number 19. Say the name of each picture. Then fill in the circle under the letter for the sound that you hear at the beginning of each picture name.

Phonics
Initial /r/r, Final /d/d

Turn to page 11.
Check to see that all the children are on the correct page.

Point to number 20.
Check to see that all the children are at the correct place.

We will continue in the same way for the first picture on this page. Say the name of the picture. Then fill in the circle under the letter for the sound that you hear at the beginning of the picture name.

Now point to number 21.

Check to see that all the children are at the correct place.

Now we are going to listen for the sound at the end of the word. Say the name of the picture. Then fill in the circle under the letter for the sound that you hear at the end of the picture name.

Phonics

Review Word Families -at, -an

Turn to page 12.

Check to see that all the children are on the correct page.

Point to number 22.

Check to see that all the children are at the correct place.

Look at the three pictures in this row. Two pictures end with the same sound. The other picture does not belong. Say the name of each picture. Listen for the sound at the end of each word. Then fill in the circle under the picture that does not belong.

Does anyone have any questions?

Point to number 23.

Check to see that all the children are at the correct place.

We will continue in the same way. Look at the three pictures in this row. Two pictures end with the same sound. The other picture does not belong. Say the name of each picture. Listen for the sound at the end of each word. Then fill in the circle under the picture that does not belong.

Concept Words

Sequence Words: First, Next, Last

Turn to page 13.

Check to see that all the children are on the correct page.

Point to the letter S.

Check to see that all the children are at the correct place.

Look at the three pictures in this row. They show what happened <u>first</u>, what happened <u>next</u>, and what happened <u>last</u>, but they are out of order. Which picture shows what happened <u>first</u>? That's right, the middle picture shows a mom mixing the cookie dough.What happened <u>next</u>? Fill in the circle below the picture that shows what happened <u>next</u>. What is the answer? That's right, <u>next</u>, the mom puts a tray of cookies in the oven. The third picture shows what happened <u>last</u>, so that is not the correct answer. You should have filled in the circle with an <u>a</u> inside because it shows what happened <u>next</u>.

Check to see that each child has filled in the circle with an <u>a</u> inside.

Does anyone have any questions?

Point to number 24.

Check to see that all the children are at the correct place.

We will continue in the same way. Listen for the words that tell the order and then fill in the circle below the correct picture. Look at the three pictures in this row. They show what happened <u>first</u>, what happened <u>next</u>, and what happened <u>last</u>, but they are out of order. Which picture shows what happened <u>last</u>?

Does anyone have any questions?

Concept Words

Position Words: First, Next, Last

Turn to page 14.

Check to see that all the children are on the correct page.

Point to number 25.

Check to see that all the children are at the correct place.

We will continue in the same way. Listen for the words that tell the order and then fill in the circle below the correct picture. Look at the three pictures in this row. Which picture shows what happened <u>first</u>?

Point to number 26.

Check to see that all the children are at the correct place.

We will continue in the same way. Listen for the words that tell the order and then fill in the circle below the correct picture. Look at the three pictures in this row. Which picture shows what happened <u>next</u>?

Name _____

Date _____

Unit
Assessment

TESTED SKILLS AND STRATEGIES

- Listening Comprehension
- Comprehension
- High-Frequency Words
- Phonemic Awareness
- Phonics
- Concept Words

Macmillan
McGraw-Hill

Name _____

S.

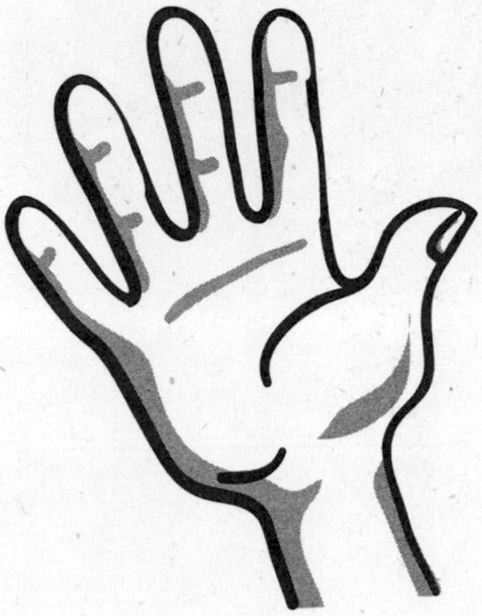

(a) 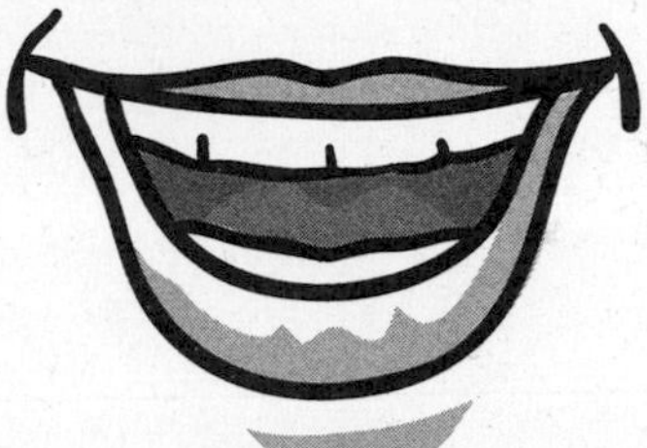 (b) 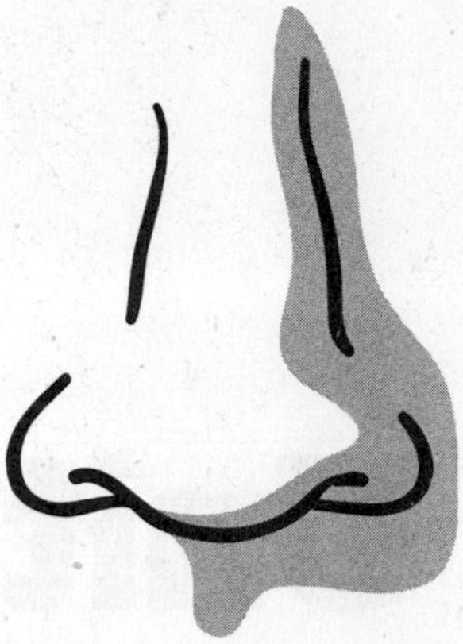 (c)

I.

(a)  (b)  (c)

2.

you	the	you	can
	ⓐ	ⓑ	ⓒ

3.

1	2	3
ⓐ	ⓑ	ⓒ

Name _____

4.

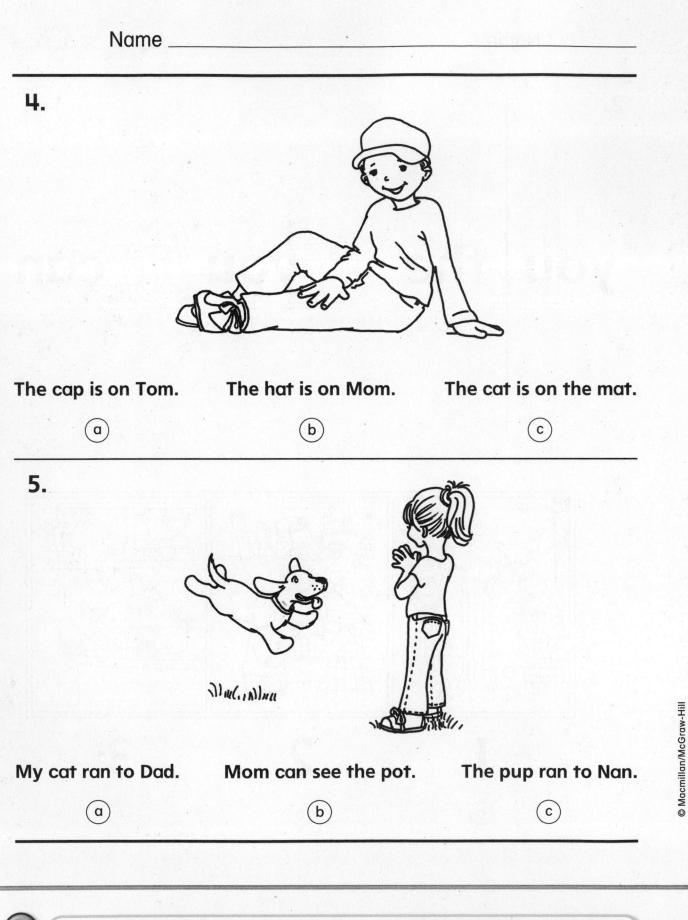

The cap is on Tom.　　　The hat is on Mom.　　　The cat is on the mat.

ⓐ　　　　　　　　　ⓑ　　　　　　　　　ⓒ

5.

My cat ran to Dad.　　　Mom can see the pot.　　　The pup ran to Nan.

ⓐ　　　　　　　　　ⓑ　　　　　　　　　ⓒ

Name _____

6.

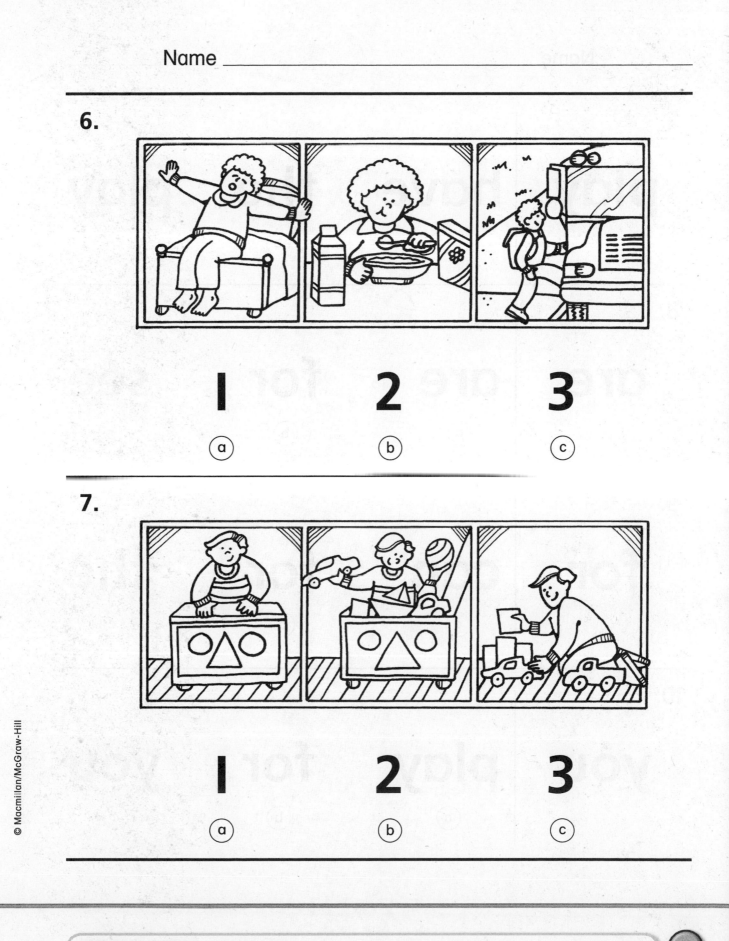

1	2	3
ⓐ	ⓑ	ⓒ

7.

1	2	3
ⓐ	ⓑ	ⓒ

Name ______________________________

S.

play	have (a)	the (b)	play (c)

8.

are	are (a)	for (b)	see (c)

9.

for	can (a)	for (b)	the (c)

10.

you	play (a)	for (b)	you (c)

Name _____

S.
a
b
c

II.
a
b
c

I2.
a
b
c

Name _____

13.

a   b   c

14.

a   b   c

15.

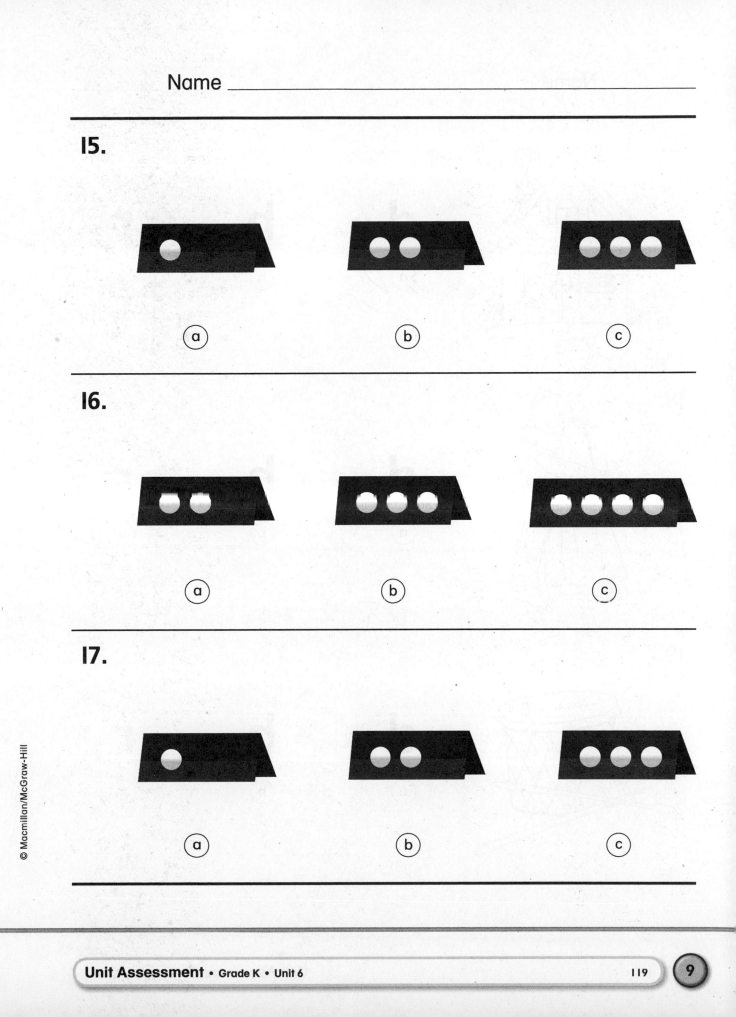

ⓐ   ⓑ   ⓒ

16.

ⓐ   ⓑ   ⓒ

17.

ⓐ   ⓑ   ⓒ

Name _____

S.

d   h   r

ⓐ   ⓑ   ⓒ

18.

d   h   r

ⓐ   ⓑ   ⓒ

19.

d   h   r

ⓐ   ⓑ   ⓒ

20.

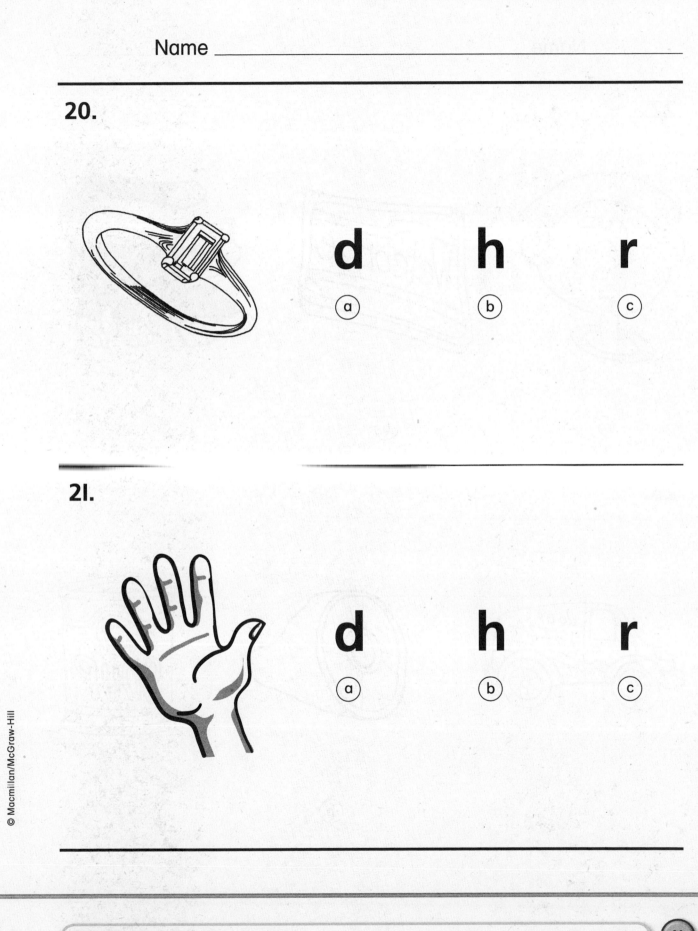

d   h   r

ⓐ   ⓑ   ⓒ

21.

d   h   r

ⓐ   ⓑ   ⓒ

22.

      ⓐ   ⓑ   ⓒ

23.

Welcome

Joe's PIZZA

SOUP

      ⓐ   ⓑ   ⓒ

S.

a    b    c

24.

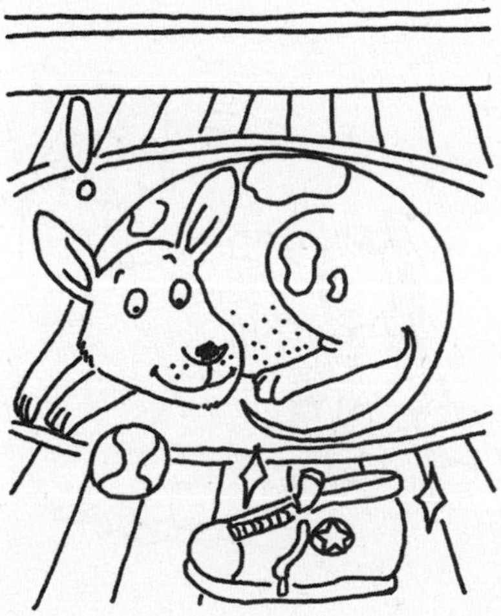

a    b    c

25.

ⓐ   ⓑ   ⓒ

26.

ⓐ   ⓑ   ⓒ

Kindergarten • Unit 6

Student Evaluation Chart

TESTED SKILLS	Number Correct	Percent Correct
Listening Comprehension	/3	%
Identify main idea and details, 1		
High-frequency word, 2		
Comprehension	/4	%
Retell, 3, 6, 7		
Identify main idea and details, 4, 5		
High Frequency Words	/3	%
are, 8		
for, 9		
you, 10		
Phonemic Awareness	/7	%
Phoneme isolation, 11, 12		
Phoneme blending, 13, 14		
Phoneme segmentation, 15, 16, 17		
Phonics	/6	%
Initial /h/h, 18		
Initial and final /d/d, 19, 21		
Initial /r/r, 20		
Word families -at, -an, 22, 23		
Concept Words	/3	%
Sequence words: first, next, last, 24, 25, 26		
Total Unit Test Score	/26	%

Listening Comprehension

Identify Setting

You are going to hear a story. After I read the story, I will ask you a few questions. Listen carefully. We will begin now.

Getting Ready for Grandma

Grandma is coming for a visit this week. She comes to see us every spring. Mom tells us what we can do to help get everything ready. Everyone has a job to do. Mom puts clean sheets on the bed and Dad bakes an apple pie. My sister picks up her toys and I vacuum the rug. The last thing we do is put fresh flowers in a vase on the table. Now everything is ready and clean for Grandma's visit.

Turn to page 2.

Check to see that all the children are on the correct page.

Point to the letter S.

Hold up page 2, pointing to the letter S for the children to see.

I will read a question. Listen to the question as I read it aloud: What does Mom do to get ready for the visit? Now look at the three pictures in this row. Fill in the circle under the right picture. What is the answer?

Have a child provide the answer.

That's right. The first picture in the row shows Mom putting clean sheets on the bed. You should have filled in the circle with an a inside.

Check to see that each child has filled in the correct circle.

Does anyone have any questions?

Now I will read the story again. Listen carefully.
Read the story aloud again.

Now point to number 1.
Check to see that all the children are at the correct place.

Now I'm going to read another question. Listen to the question as I read it aloud: Where is Grandma visiting in the story? Now look at the three pictures in this row. Fill in the circle under the picture that shows the answer to the question.

Listening Comprehension

Distinguish Between Fantasy and Reality; High-Frequency Words

Turn to page 3.
Check to see that all the children are on the correct page.

Point to number 2.
Check to see that all the children are at the correct place.

Look at the pictures in this row. Two pictures show something that might really happen and one picture is make-believe. Fill in the circle under the picture that shows something make-believe.

Point to number 3.
Check to see that all the children are at the correct place.

Look at the first word in this row. Now look at the other three words in the row. Fill in the circle under the word that is the same as the first word in the row.

Comprehension

Identify Main Idea and Details

Turn to page 4.
Check to see that all the children are on the correct page.

Point to number 4.
Check to see that all the children are at the correct place.

Read the sentences. Fill in the circle under the sentence that tells what the picture is all about.

Point to number 5.
Check to see that all the children are at the correct place.

Read the sentences. Fill in the circle under the sentence that tells what the picture is all about.

Comprehension

Identify Setting; Distinguish Between Fantasy and Reality

Turn to page 5.
Check to see that all the children are on the correct page.

Point to number 6.
Check to see that all the children are at the correct place.

Look at the three pictures in this row. Fill in the circle under the picture that shows where a clown belongs.

Point to number 7.
Check to see that all the children are at the correct place.

Look at the pictures in this row. One picture shows something that might really happen and two pictures are make-believe. Fill in the circle under the picture that shows something that might really happen.

High-Frequency Words

this, do, and, what

Turn to page 6.
Check to see that all the children are on the correct page.

Point to the letter S.
Check to see that all the children are at the correct place. Write the first word from row S on the board followed by the three word choices with their answer circles (a,b,c). Hold up page 7, pointing to the first word in the row so the children can see.

Look at the first word in the row. What is the word? That's right, the word is <u>for</u>. Look at the other three words in the row. I am going to fill in the circle under the word where I see it in the same row.
Fill in the circle <u>b</u> under the word <u>for</u> on the board.

The circle I filled in is <u>b</u> under the word <u>for</u>. It is the same as the first word in the row. Now you will do the same on your paper. Look at the first word in row S. Now fill in the circle under the word where you see it in the same row.
Check to see that all the children have filled in the circle <u>b</u> under the word <u>for</u> in row S.

Does anyone have any questions?

We will continue in the same way. Follow the same instructions for the next four rows. Look at the first word in each row. Then fill in the circle under the word where you see it in the same row.

Phonemic Awareness

Phoneme Isolation

Turn to page 7.
Check to see that all the children are on the correct page.

Point to the letter S.
Hold up page 7, pointing to the first row for all the children to see. Check to see that all the children are at the correct place.

I will say a word: <u>end</u>, /e/ /nd/. What is the beginning sound in /e/ /nd/? Listen to these answer choices: <u>tent</u>, <u>egg</u>, <u>rain</u>. Which answer choice has the same beginning sound as /e/ /nd/? That's right. The word <u>egg</u> has the same beginning sound as <u>end</u>. Fill in the circle under the picture of the <u>egg</u> because it has the same beginning sound as <u>end</u>.
Check to see that all the children have filled in the circle <u>b</u> under the picture of the <u>egg</u>.

Does anyone have any questions?

Now point to number 12.
Check to see that all the children are at the correct place.

Look at question 12. I will say a word: <u>bed</u>, /b/ /ed/. What is the beginning sound in /b/ /ed/? Listen to these answer choices: <u>daisy</u>, <u>rabbit</u>, <u>banana</u>. Fill in the circle under the picture that has the same beginning sound as /b/ /ed/.

Now point to number 13.
Check to see that all the children are at the correct place.

Look at question 13. I will say a word: <u>let</u>, /l/ /e/ /t/. What is the beginning sound in /l/ /e/ /t/? Listen to these answer choices: <u>leaf</u>, <u>bear</u>, <u>rattle</u>. Fill in the circle under the picture that has the same beginning sound as /l/ /e/ /t/.

Phonemic Awareness
Phoneme Blending

Turn to page 8.
Check to see that all the children are on the correct page.

Point to number 14.
Check to see that all the children are at the correct place.

Look at question 14. I will say a word in parts: /l/ /i/ /d/. What word do you make when you put these sounds together? Listen to these answer choices: doll, lid, lip. Fill in the circle under the picture that has the same sounds as /l/ /i/ /d/.

Now point to number 15.
Check to see that all the children are at the correct place.

Look at question 15. I will say a word in parts: /b/ /e/ /lt/. What word do you make when you put these sounds together? Listen to these answer choices: bell, melt, belt. Fill in the circle under the picture that has the same sounds as /b/ /e/ /lt/.

Phonemic Awareness
Phoneme Segmentation

Turn to page 9.
Point to number 16.
Check to see that all the children are at the correct place.

Look at question 16. Listen while I say the sounds in the word end: /e/ /n/ /d/. How many sounds do you hear in the word /e/ /n/ /d? Say the word slowly. Fill in the circle under the picture that shows how many sounds you hear in /e/ /n/ /d/.

Point to number 17.
Check to see that all the children are at the correct place.

Look at question 17. Listen while I say the sounds in the word best: /b/ /e/ /s/ /t/. How many sounds do you hear in the word /b/ /e/ /s/ /t/? Say the word slowly. Fill in the circle under the picture that shows how many sounds you hear in /b/ /e/ /s/ /t/.

Point to number 18.
Check to see that all the children are at the correct place.

Look at question 18. Listen while I say the sounds in the word lick: /l/ /i/ /k/. How many sounds do you hear in the word /l/ /i/ /k/? Say the word slowly. Fill in the circle under the picture that shows how many sounds you hear in /l/ /i/ /k/.

Phonics
Short /e/e, Initial /b/b

Turn to page 10.
Check to see that all the children are on the correct page.

Point to the letter S in the first row.
Check to see that all the children are at the correct place. Hold up page 10, pointing to the picture of the elephant in the first row.

Say the name of the picture. That's right, it is a picture of an elephant. What beginning sound did you hear? Did you hear the /e/ sound in elephant? Fill in the circle under the letter e.
Check to see that each child filled in the correct circle.

Does anyone have any questions?

We will continue in the same way on this page for number 19 and number 20. Say the name of each picture. Then fill in the circle under the letter for the sound that you hear at the beginning of each picture name.

Phonics
Initial /l/l, Final /b/b

Turn to page 11.
Check to see that all the children are on the correct page.

Point to number 21.
Check to see that all the children are at the correct place.

We will continue in the same way for the first picture on this page. Say the name of the picture. Then fill in the circle under the letter for the sound that you hear at the beginning of the picture name.

Now point to number 22.
Check to see that all the children are at the correct place.

Now we are going to listen for the sound at the end of the word. Say the name of the picture. Then fill in the circle under the letter for the sound that you hear at the end of the picture name.

Phonics
Review Word Families -it, -ip

Turn to page 12.
Check to see that all the children are on the correct page.

Point to number 23.
Check to see that all the children are at the correct place.

Look at the three pictures in this row. Two pictures end with the same sound. The other picture does not belong. Say the name of each picture. Listen for the sound at the end of each word. Then fill in the circle under the picture that does not belong.

Does anyone have any questions?

Point to number 24.
Check to see that all the children are at the correct place.

We will continue in the same way. Look at the three pictures in this row. Two pictures end with the same sound. The other picture does not belong. Say the name of each picture. Listen for the sound at the end of each word. Then fill in the circle under the picture that does not belong.

Concept Words
Words that Compare: Tallest

Turn to page 13.
Check to see that all the children are on the correct page.

Point to the letter S.
Check to see that all the children are at the correct place.

Look at the three pictures of tall buildings in this row. They are different sizes. We are going to compare the sizes. The first building is <u>taller</u> than the second building. Which picture shows the <u>tallest</u> building? Fill in the circle below the picture that shows the <u>tallest</u> building. What is the answer? That's right, the building in the last picture is the <u>tallest</u> building. You should have filled in the circle with a <u>c</u> inside because it shows the <u>tallest</u> building.

Check to see that each child has filled in the circle with a <u>c</u> inside.

Does anyone have any questions?

Point to number 25.
Check to see that all the children are at the correct place.

We will continue in the same way. Listen for the word that compares and then fill in the circle below the correct picture. Look at the three pictures of trees in this row. Which picture shows the <u>tallest</u> tree? Fill in the circle below the picture of the <u>tallest</u> tree.

Does anyone have any questions?

Concept Words
Words that Compare: Smallest, Longest

Turn to page 14.
Check to see that all the children are on the correct page.

Point to number 26.
Check to see that all the children are at the correct place.

We will continue in the same way. Listen for the word that compares and then fill in the circle below the correct picture. Look at the three pictures of animals in this row. Which picture shows the <u>smallest</u> animal? Fill in the circle below the picture of the <u>smallest</u> animal.

Point to number 27.
Check to see that all the children are at the correct place.

We will continue in the same way. Listen for the word that compares and then fill in the circle below the correct picture. Look at the three pictures of girls in this row. Which picture shows the girl with the <u>longest</u> hair? Fill in the circle below the picture of the girl with the <u>longest</u> hair.

Name _____

Date _____

Treasures

Unit Assessment

TESTED SKILLS AND STRATEGIES

- **Listening Comprehension**
- **Comprehension**
- **High-Frequency Words**
- **Phonemic Awareness**
- **Phonics**
- **Concept Words**

Macmillan McGraw-Hill

S.

ⓐ   ⓑ   ⓒ

I.

ⓐ   ⓑ   ⓒ

2.

ⓐ   ⓑ   ⓒ

3.

this like   this   have

ⓐ   ⓑ   ⓒ

4.

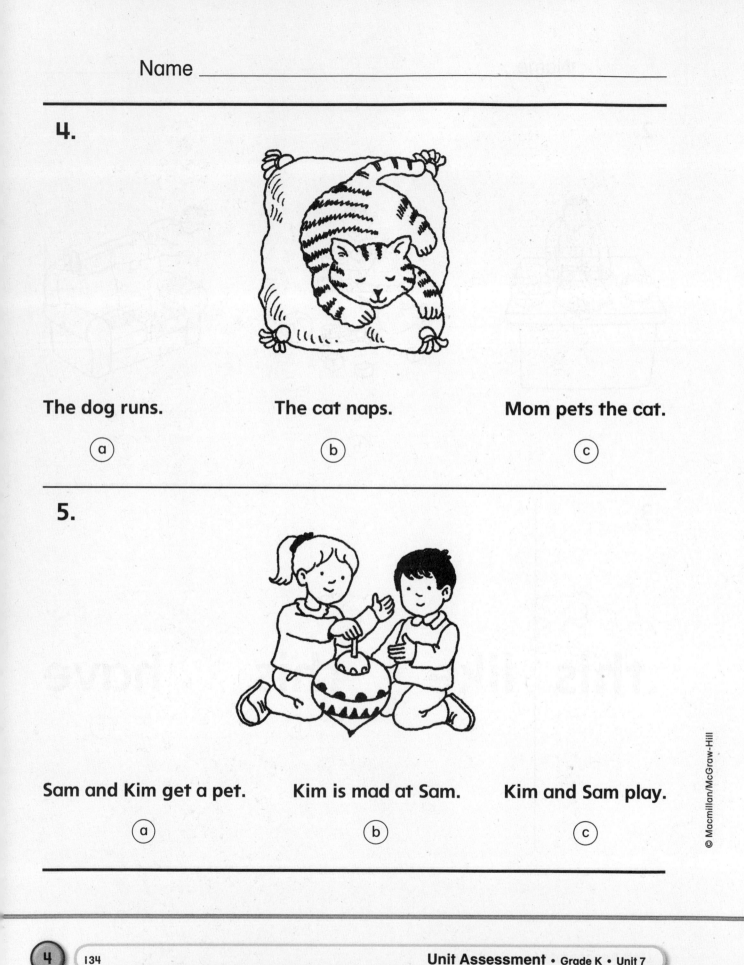

The dog runs.

The cat naps.

Mom pets the cat.

(a)

(b)

(c)

5.

Sam and Kim get a pet.

Kim is mad at Sam.

Kim and Sam play.

(a)

(b)

(c)

© Macmillan/McGraw-Hill

6.

(a)   (b)   (c)

7.

(a)   (b)   (c)

s.

for | see   for   are
     ⓐ   ⓑ   ⓒ

8.

this | the   see   this
     ⓐ   ⓑ   ⓒ

9.

do | do   to   go
     ⓐ   ⓑ   ⓒ

10.

and | can   and   are
     ⓐ   ⓑ   ⓒ

11.

what | have   like   what
     ⓐ   ⓑ   ⓒ

S.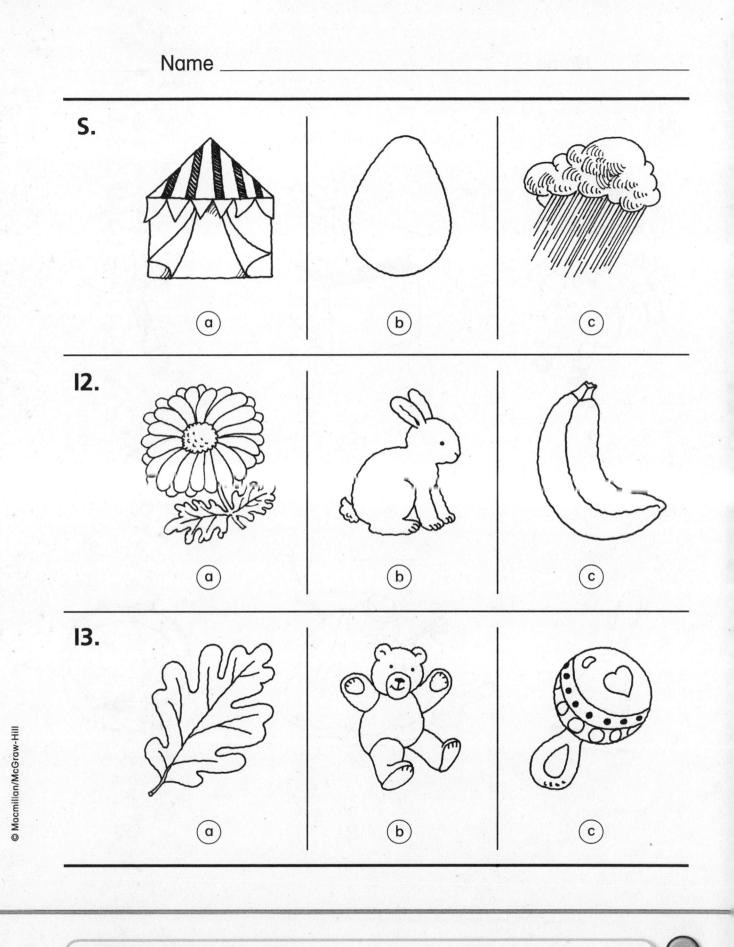

ⓐ ⓑ ⓒ

12.

ⓐ ⓑ ⓒ

13.

ⓐ ⓑ ⓒ

14.

(a)   (b)   (c)

15.

(a)   (b)   (c)

Name _____

16.

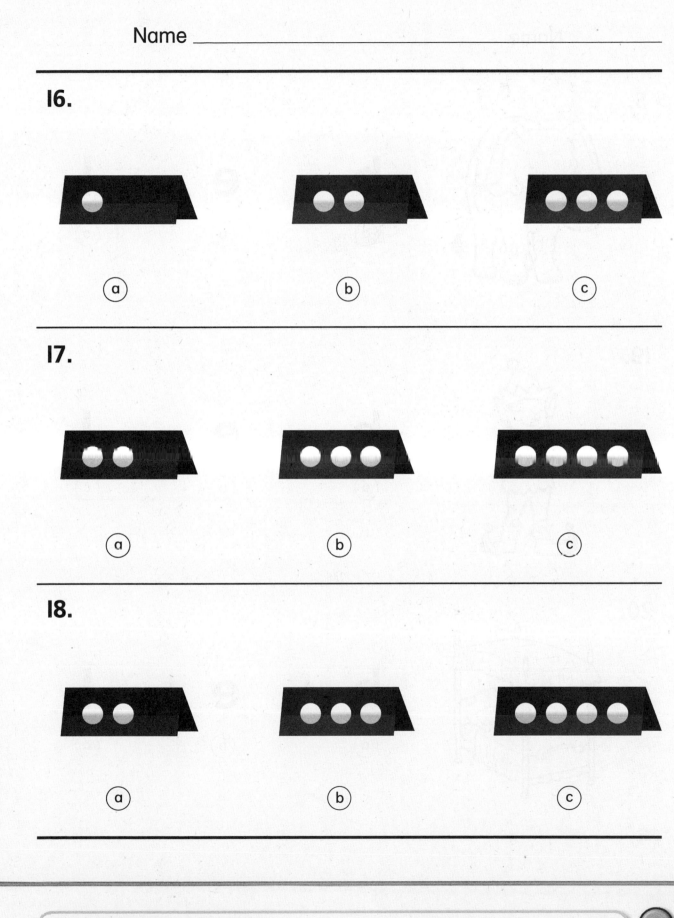

© Macmillan/McGraw-Hill

S.

b
(a)

e
(b)

l
(c)

19.

b
(a)

e
(b)

l
(c)

20.

b
(a)

e
(b)

l
(c)

21.

b   e   l

(a)   (b)   (c)

22.

b   e   l

(a)   (b)   (c)

23.

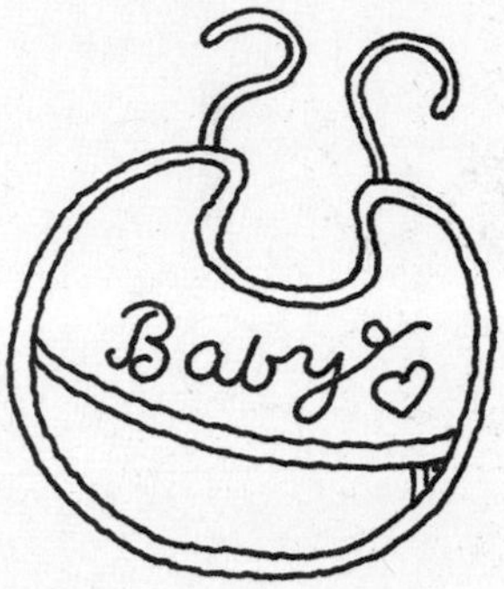

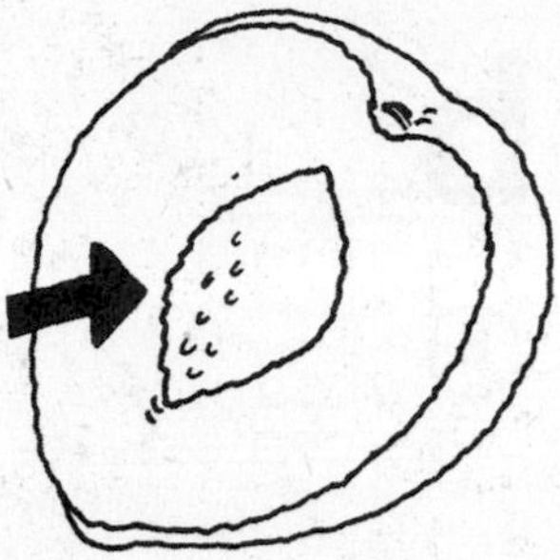

(a)　　　　　　(b)　　　　　　(c)

24.

(a)　　　　　　(b)　　　　　　(c)

Name _____

S.

   ⓐ   ⓑ   ⓒ

25.

   ⓐ   ⓑ   ⓒ

26.

27.

ⓐ   ⓑ   ⓒ

Name _____

Student Evaluation Chart

TESTED SKILLS	Number Correct	Percent Correct
Listening Comprehension	/3	%
Identify setting, 1		
Distinguish between fantasy and reality, 2		
High-frequency word, 3		
Comprehension	/4	%
Identify main idea and details, 4, 5		
Identify setting, 6		
Distinguish between fantasy and reality, 7		
High Frequency Words	/4	%
this, 8		
do, 9		
and, 10		
what, 11		
Phonemic Awareness	/7	%
Phoneme isolation, 12, 13		
Phoneme blending, 14, 15		
Phoneme segmentation, 16, 17, 18		
Phonics	/6	%
Initial /e/e, 16		
Initial and final /b/b, 17, 19		
Initial /l/l, 18		
Word families -it, -ip, 20, 21		
Concept Words	/3	%
Words that compare: tallest, smallest, longest, 22, 23, 24		
Total Unit Test Score	/27	%

Listening Comprehension
Identify Sequence of Events

You are going to hear a story. After I read the story, I will ask you a few questions. Listen carefully. We will begin now.

How Does a Flower Grow?

Have you ever said, "I wonder how a flower grows"? There are many kinds of flowers, but each flower was once a little seed. Here is how a flower grows: First, the seed is planted in the dirt. Next, it needs water and plenty of sunshine. After a few days, you may be able to see a little green leaf starting to show. Then, more leaves will appear and the flower will keep growing. A bud will form. Finally, the bud will open up and you will see a pretty flower!

Turn to page 2.
Check to see that all the children are on the correct page.

Point to the letter S.
Hold up page 2, pointing to the letter S for the children to see.

I will read a question. Listen to the question as I read it aloud: In this story, what happens first to make a flower grow? Now look at the three pictures in this row. Fill in the circle under the correct picture. What is the answer?
Have a child provide the answer.

That's right. The second picture in the row shows a seed being planted in the dirt. You should have filled in the circle with a b inside.
Check to see that each child has filled in the correct circle.

Does anyone have any questions?

Now I will read the story again. Listen carefully.
Read the story aloud again.

Now point to number 1.
Check to see that all the children are at the correct place.

Now I'm going to read another question. Listen to the question as I read it aloud: After the seed is planted, what happens next? Look at the three pictures in this row. Fill in the circle under the picture that shows the answer to the question.

Listening Comprehension
High-Frequency Words

Turn to page 3.
Check to see that all the children are on the correct page.

Point to number 2.
Check to see that all the children are at the correct place.

Look at the first word in this row. Now look at the other three words in the row. Fill in the circle under the word that is the same as the first word in the row.

Comprehension
Draw Conclusions

Point to number 3.
Check to see that all the children are at the correct place.

Look at the pictures in this row. Fill in the circle under the picture that shows what a flowerpot looks like after three seeds grow.

Comprehension
Identify Sequence of Events

Turn to page 4.
Check to see that all the children are on the correct page.

Point to number 4.
Check to see that all the children are at the correct place.

Look at the three pictures in this row. Fill in the circle under the picture that shows what happened <u>first</u>.

Point to number 5.
Check to see that all the children are at the correct place.

Look at the three pictures in this row. Fill in the circle under the picture that shows what happened <u>last</u>.

Comprehension

Draw Conclusions; Retell

Turn to page 5.

Check to see that all the children are on the correct page.

Point to number 6.

Check to see that all the children are at the correct place.

Look at the pictures in this row. Fill in the circle under the picture that shows someone whom you think is going to the beach.

Point to number 7.

Check to see that all the children are at the correct place.

Look at each picture. These pictures tell a story. Listen as I read three sentences. One sentence will tell what the story is about. Fill in the circle under the number of the sentence that tells what the story is about. Now listen carefully while I read the three sentences. Number 1: Jimmy gets ready for a bike ride. Number 2: Jimmy goes to a birthday party. Number 3: Jimmy goes to bed.

High-Frequency Words

little, said, here, was

Turn to page 6.

Check to see that all the children are on the correct page.

Point to the letter S.

Check to see that all the children are at the correct place. Write the first word from row S on the board followed by the three word choices with their answer circles (a,b,c). Hold up page 7, pointing to the first word in the row so the children can see.

Look at the first word in the row. What is the word? That's right, the word is <u>what</u>. Look at the other three words in the row. I am going to fill in the circle under the word where I see it in the same row.

Fill in the circle <u>a</u> under the word <u>what</u> on the board.

The circle I filled in is <u>a</u> under the word <u>what</u>. It is the same as the first word in the row. Now you will do the same on your paper. Look at the first word in row S. Now fill in the circle under the word where you see it in the same row.

Check to see that all the children have filled in the circle <u>a</u> under the word <u>what</u> in row S.

Does anyone have any questions?

We will continue in the same way. Follow the same instructions for the next four rows. Look at the first word in each row. Then fill in the circle under the word where you see it in the same row.

Phonemic Awareness

Phoneme Isolation

Turn to page 7.

Check to see that all the children are on the correct page.

Point to the letter S.

Hold up page 7, pointing to the first row for all the children to see.

Check to see that all the children are at the correct place.

I will say a word: <u>kind</u>, /k/ /i/ /t/. What is the beginning sound in /k/ /i/ /t/? Listen to these answer choices: <u>kangaroo</u>, <u>duck</u>, <u>garden</u>. Which answer choice has the same beginning sound as /k/ /i/ /t/? That's right. The word <u>kangaroo</u> has the same beginning sound as /k/ /i/ /t/. Fill in the circle under the picture of the <u>kangaroo</u> because it has the same beginning sound as /k/ /i/ /t/.

Check to see that all the children have filled in the circle <u>a</u> under the picture of the <u>kangaroo</u> in row S.

Does anyone have any questions?

Now point to number 12.

Check to see that all the children are at the correct place.

Look at question 12. I will say a word: <u>keep</u>, /k/ /ē/ /p/. What is the beginning sound in /k/ /ē/ /p/? Listen to these answer choices: <u>chair</u>, <u>kitten</u>, <u>pencil</u>. Fill in the circle under the picture that has the same beginning sound as /k/ /ē/ /p/.

Now point to number 13.

Check to see that all the children are at the correct place.

Look at question 13. I will say a word: <u>upon</u>, /u/ /p/ /o/ /n/. What is the beginning sound in /u/ /p/ /o/ /n/? Listen to these answer choices: <u>umbrella</u>, <u>pickle</u>, <u>clock</u>. Fill in the circle under the picture that has the same beginning sound as /u/ /p/ /o/ /n/.

Phonemic Awareness

Phoneme Blending

Turn to page 8.

Check to see that all the children are on the correct page.

Point to number 14.

Check to see that all the children are at the correct place.

*Look at question 14. I will say a word in parts:
/k/ /i/ /s/. What word do you make when you put
these sounds together? Listen to these answer
choices:* <u>kiss</u>, <u>list</u>, <u>sick</u>. *Fill in the circle under
the picture that has the same sounds as /k/ /i/ /s/.*

Now point to number 15.

Check to see that all the children are at the correct place.

*Look at question 15. I will say a word in parts:
/b/ /u/ /d/. What word do you make when you put
these sounds together? Listen to these answer
choices:* <u>bed</u>, <u>bag</u>, <u>bud</u>. *Fill in the circle under the
picture that has the same sounds as /b/ /u/ /d/.*

Phonemic Awareness

Phoneme Segmentation

Turn to page 9.

Check to see that all the children are on the correct page.

Point to number 16.

Check to see that all the children are at the correct place.

*Look at question 16. Listen while I say the sounds in the
word* <u>kid</u>: /k/ /i/ /d/. *How many sounds do you hear in
the word /k/ /i/ /d/? Say the word slowly. Fill in the circle
under the picture that shows how many sounds you hear
in /k/ /i/ /d/.*

Point to number 17.

Check to see that all the children are at the correct place.

*Look at question 17. Listen while I say the sounds in the
word* <u>up</u>: /u/ /p/. *How many sounds do you hear in the
word /u/ /p/? Say the word slowly. Fill in the circle under
the picture that shows how many sounds you hear in
/u/ /p/.*

Point to number 18.

Check to see that all the children are at the correct place.

*Look at question 18. Listen while I say the sounds in the
word* <u>lot</u>: /l/ /o/ /t/. *How many sounds do you hear in the
word /l/ /o/ /t/? Say the word slowly. Fill in the circle
under the picture that shows how many sounds you hear
in /l/ /o/ /t/.*

Phonics

Initial /k/k, Final /k/ck

Turn to page 10.

Check to see that all the children are on the correct page.

Point to the letter S in the first row.

**Check to see that all the children are at the correct place.
Hold up page 10, pointing to the picture of the kite in the
first row.**

*Say the name of the picture. That's right, it is a picture
of a* <u>kite</u>. *What beginning sound did you hear? Did you
hear the /k/ sound in* <u>kite</u>? *Fill in the circle under the
letter* <u>k</u>.

Check to see that each child filled in the correct circle.

Does anyone have any questions?

Point to number 19.

Check to see that all the children are at the correct place.

*We will continue in the same way on this page for
number 19. Say the name of the picture. Then fill in
the circle under the letter for the sound that you hear
at the beginning of the picture name.*

Point to number 20.

Check to see that all the children are at the correct place.

*Now we are going to listen for the sound at the end of
the word. Say the name of the picture. Then fill in the
circle under the letter for the sound that you hear at
the end of the picture name.*

Phonics

Short /u/u, Word Family -ot

Turn to page 11.

Check to see that all the children are on the correct page.

Point to number 21.

Check to see that all the children are at the correct place.

We will continue in the same way for the first picture on this page. Say the name of the picture. Then fill in the circle under the letter for the sound that you hear in the middle of the picture name.

Now point to number 22.
Check to see that all the children are at the correct place.

Look at the three pictures in this row. Two pictures end with the same sound. The other picture does not belong. Say the name of each picture. Listen for the sound at the end of each word. Then fill in the circle under the picture that does not belong.

Phonics
Word Families -op, -ick

Turn to page 12.
Check to see that all the children are on the correct page.

Point to number 23.
Check to see that all the children are at the correct place.

We will continue in the same way on this page. Look at the three pictures in this row. Two pictures end with the same sound. The other picture does not belong. Say the name of each picture. Listen for the sound at the end of each word. Then fill in the circle under the picture that does not belong.

Does anyone have any questions?

Point to number 24.
Check to see that all the children are at the correct place.

Look at the three pictures in this row. Two pictures end with the same sound. The other picture does not belong. Say the name of each picture. Listen for the sound at the end of each word. Then fill in the circle under the picture that does not belong.

Concept Words
Position Words: Top

Turn to page 13.
Check to see that all the children are on the correct page.

Point to the letter S.
Check to see that all the children are at the correct place.

Look at the three pictures of bookcases. The books are on different shelves. Which picture shows books on the top *shelf? Fill in the circle below the picture that shows books on the* top *shelf. What is the answer? That's right, the bookcase in the first picture shows books on the* top *shelf. You should have filled in the circle with an* a *inside because it shows books on the* top *shelf.*

Check to see that each child has filled in the circle with an a inside.

Does anyone have any questions?

Point to number 25.
Check to see that all the children are at the correct place.

We will continue in the same way. Listen for the position word and then fill in the circle below the correct picture. Look at the three pictures of steps in this row. Which picture shows the kitten on the top *step? Fill in the circle below the picture of the kitten on the* top *step.*

Does anyone have any questions?

Concept Words
Position Words: Middle, Bottom

Turn to page 14.
Check to see that all the children are on the correct page.

Point to number 26.
Check to see that all the children are at the correct place.

We will follow the same instructions as on the previous page. Listen for the position word and then fill in the circle below the correct picture. Look at the three pictures of trees in this row. Which picture shows the bird in the middle *of the tree? Fill in the circle below the picture of the bird in the* middle *of the tree.*

Point to number 27.
Check to see that all the children are at the correct place.

Look at the three pictures of a slide in this row. Which picture shows the boy at the bottom *of the slide? Fill in the circle below the picture of the boy at the* bottom *of the slide.*

Name _____

Date _____

Unit
Assessment

TESTED SKILLS AND STRATEGIES

- **Listening Comprehension**
- **Comprehension**
- **High-Frequency Words**
- **Phonemic Awareness**
- **Phonics**
- **Concept Words**

Mc Graw Hill **Macmillan McGraw-Hill**

S.

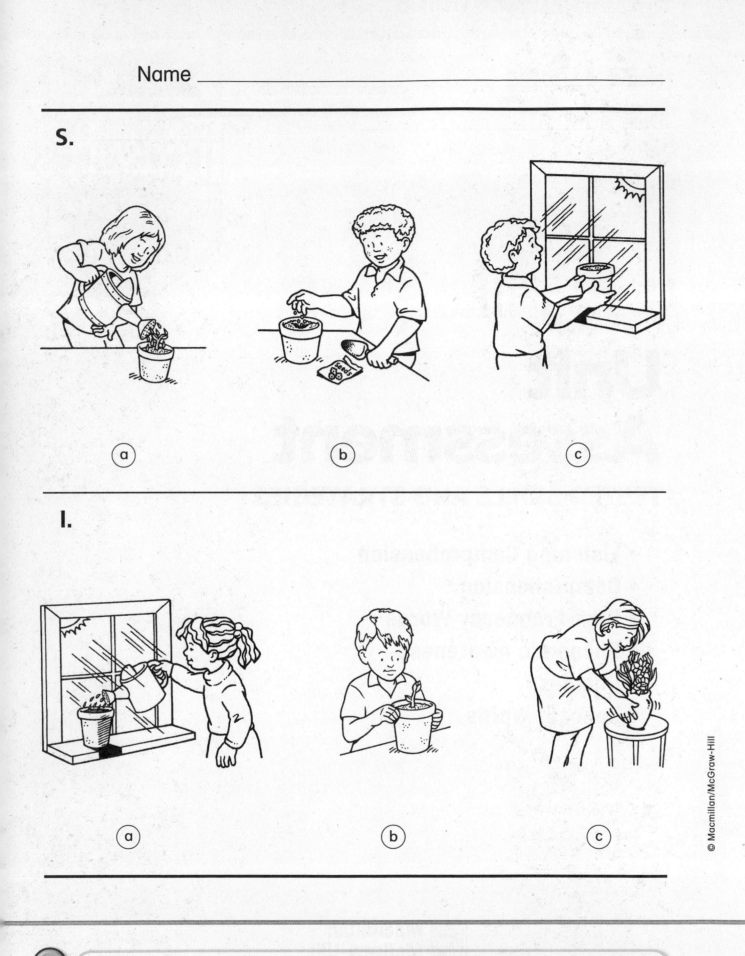

ⓐ   ⓑ   ⓒ

I.

ⓐ   ⓑ   ⓒ

© Macmillan/McGraw-Hill

2.

little | like   this   little

ⓐ   ⓑ   ⓒ

3.

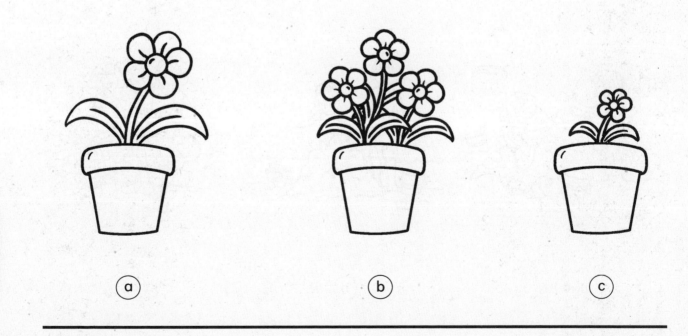

ⓐ   ⓑ   ⓒ

4.

a   b   c

5.

a   b   c

6.

ⓐ   ⓑ   ⓒ

7.

1 ⓐ   **2** ⓑ   **3** ⓒ

S.

what | what | play | have
(a) | (b) | (c)

8.

little | like | this | little
(a) | (b) | (c)

9.

said | see | this | said
(a) | (b) | (c)

10.

here | have | here | are
(a) | (b) | (c)

II.

was | was | can | what
(a) | (b) | (c)

S.
   ⓐ   ⓑ   ⓒ

12.
   ⓐ   ⓑ   ⓒ

13.
   ⓐ   ⓑ   ⓒ

Name ____________________

14.

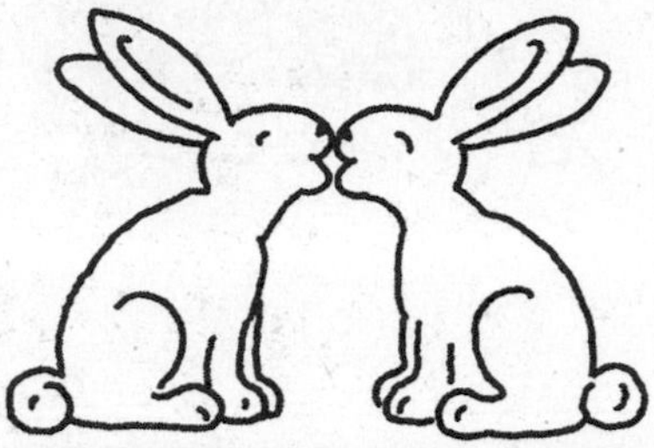

ⓐ

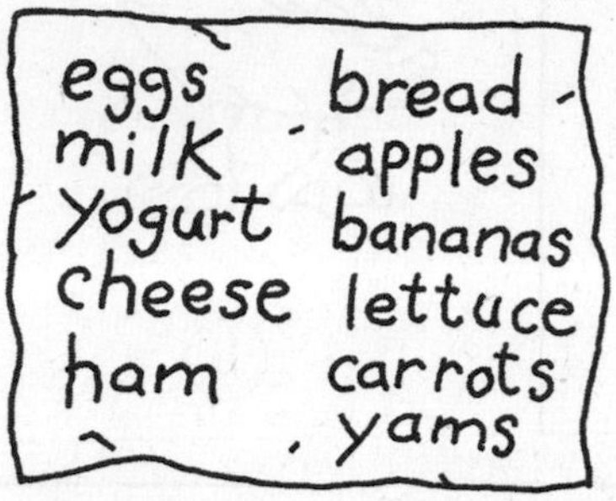
eggs
milk
yogurt
cheese
ham
bread
apples
bananas
lettuce
carrots
yams

ⓑ

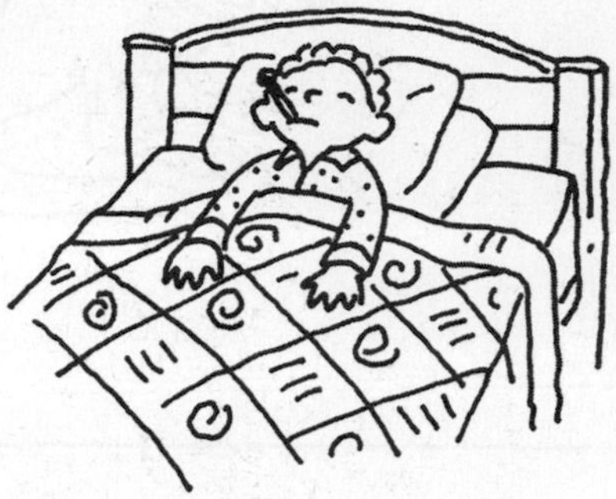

ⓒ

15.

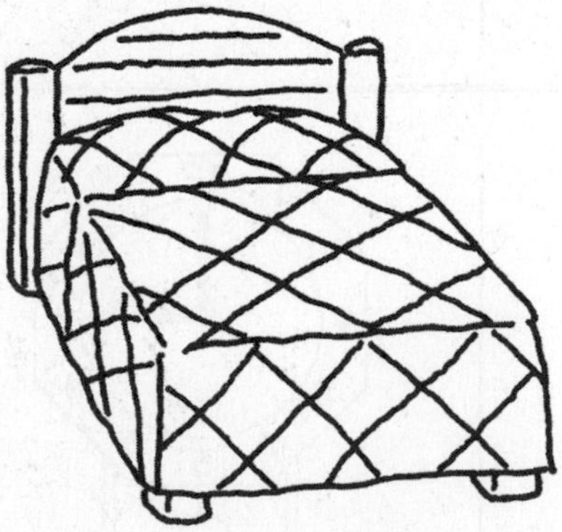

ⓐ

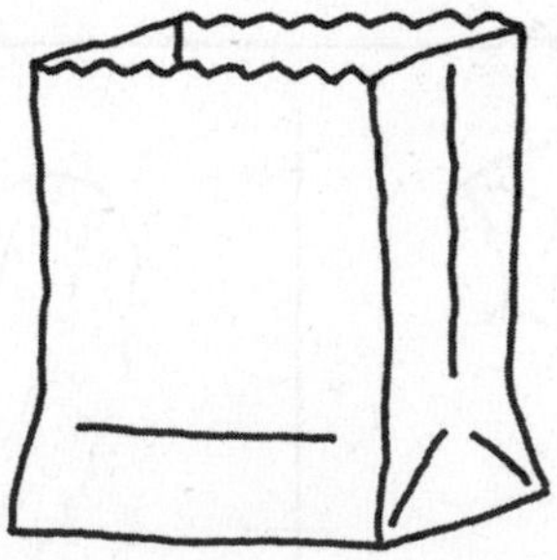

ⓑ

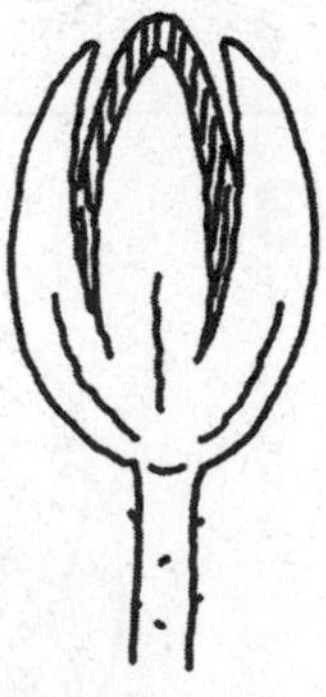

ⓒ

Name _____

16.

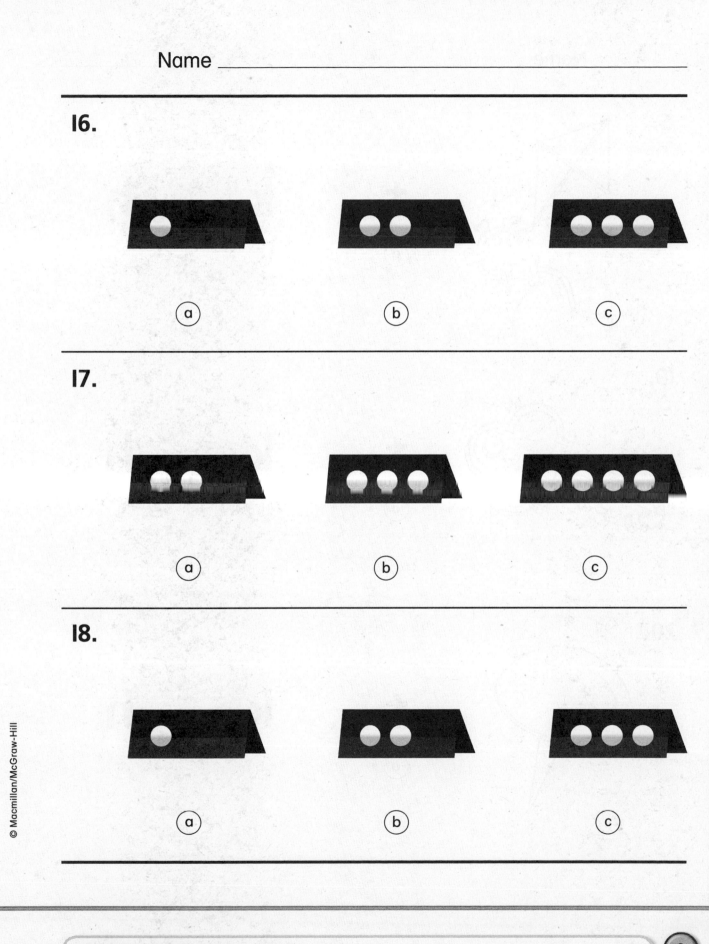

ⓐ   ⓑ   ⓒ

17.

ⓐ   ⓑ   ⓒ

18.

ⓐ   ⓑ   ⓒ

S.

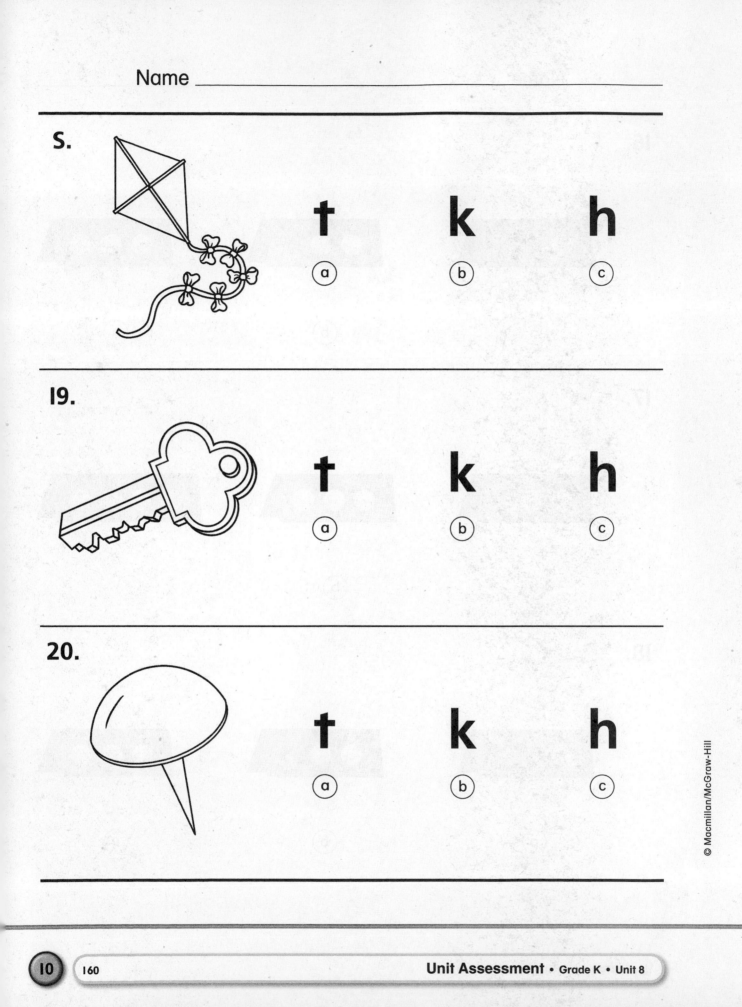

t	**k**	**h**
ⓐ	ⓑ	ⓒ

19.

t	**k**	**h**
ⓐ	ⓑ	ⓒ

20.

t	**k**	**h**
ⓐ	ⓑ	ⓒ

21.

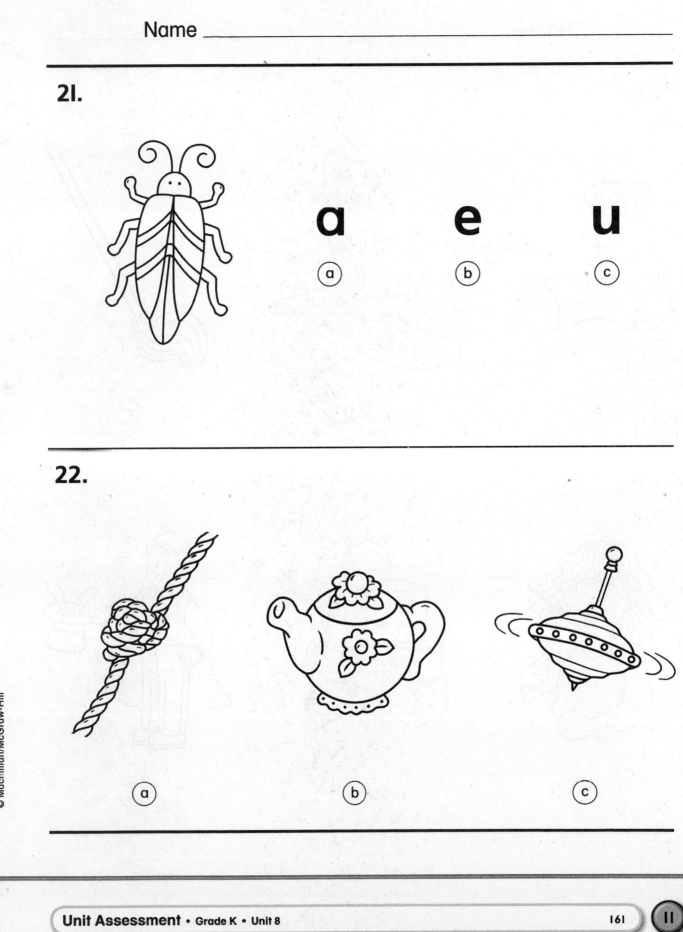

a
(a)

e
(b)

u
(c)

22.

(a)   (b)   (c)

23.

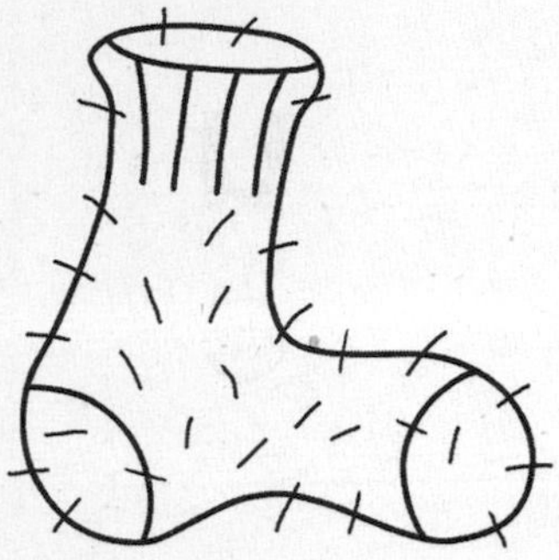

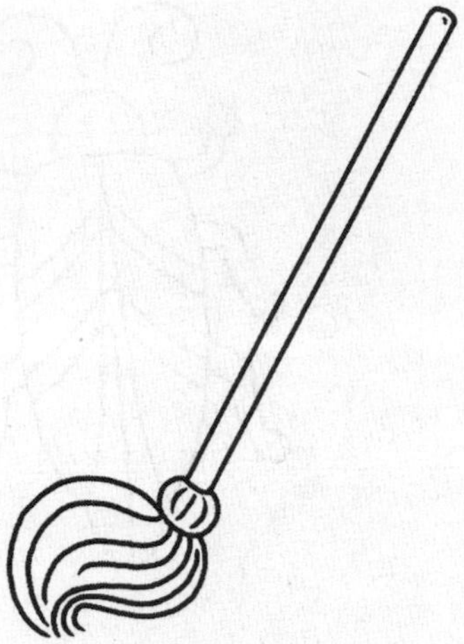

a

b

c

24.

a

b

c

S.

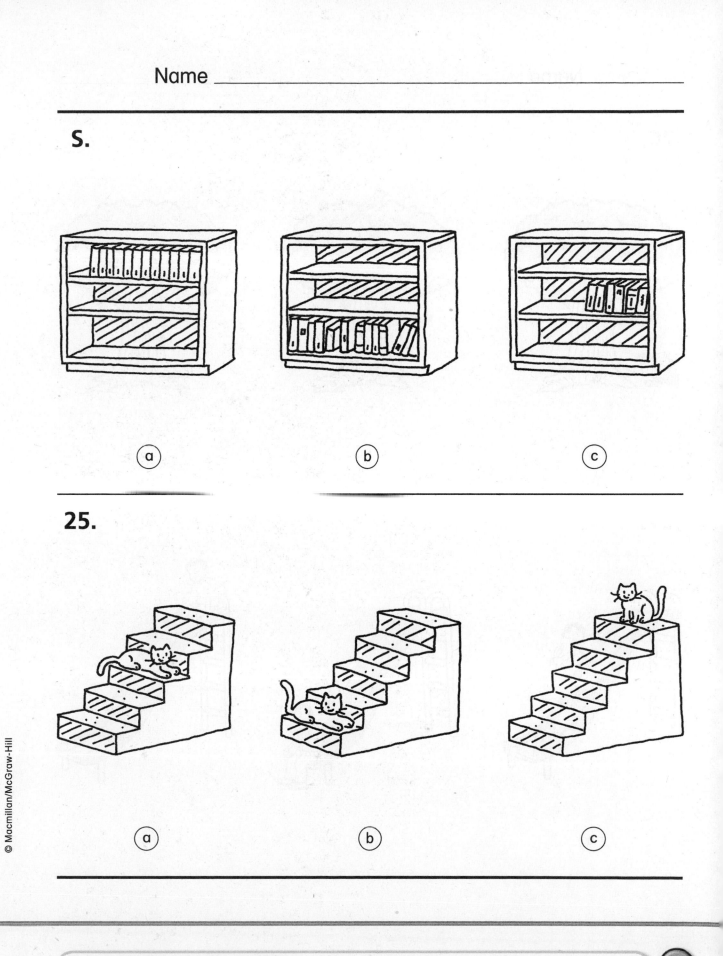

(a)   (b)   (c)

25.

(a)   (b)   (c)

26.

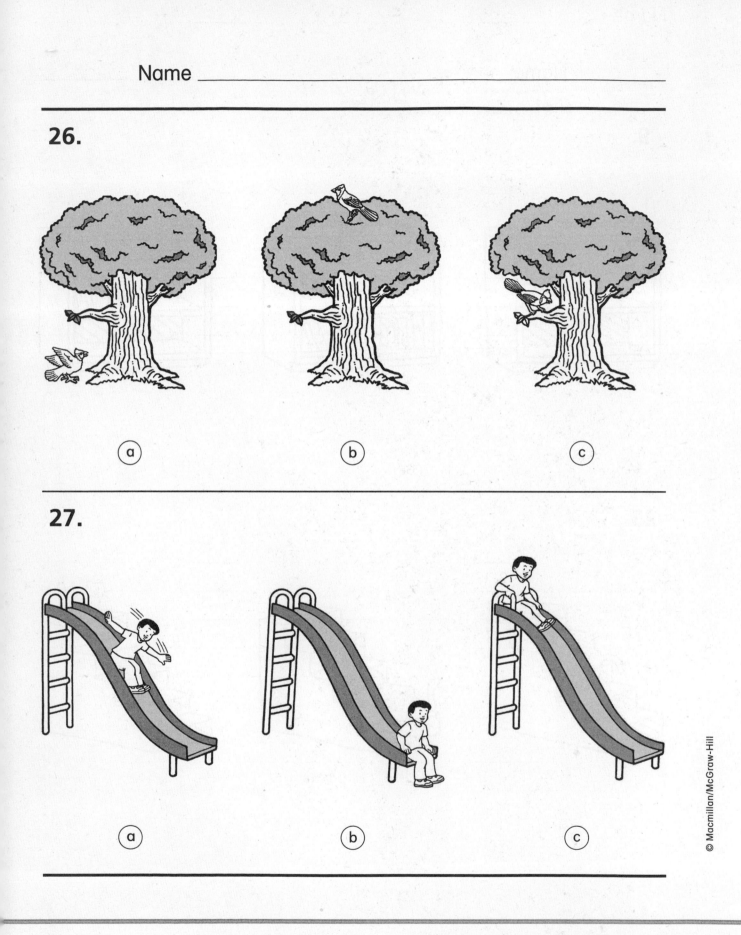

ⓐ   ⓑ   ⓒ

27.

ⓐ   ⓑ   ⓒ

Name _____

Student Evaluation Chart

TESTED SKILLS	Number Correct	Percent Correct
Listening Comprehension	/2	%
Identify sequence of events, 1		
High-frequency word, 2		
Comprehension	/5	%
Draw conclusions, 3, 6		
Identify sequence of events, 4, 5		
Retell, 7		
High Frequency Words	/4	%
little, 8		
said, 9		
here, 10		
was, 11		
Phonemic Awareness	/7	%
Phoneme isolation, 12, 13		
Phoneme blending, 14, 15		
Phoneme segmentation, 16, 17, 18		
Phonics	/6	%
Initial /k/k and final /k/ck, 19, 20		
Short /u/u, 21		
Word families -ot, -op, -ick, 22, 23, 24		
Concept Words	/3	%
Position words: top, middle, bottom, 25, 26, 27		
Total Unit Test Score	/27	%

Listening Comprehension
Distinguish Between Fantasy and Reality

You are going to hear a story. After I read the story, I will ask you a few questions. Listen carefully. We will begin now.

At the Zoo

Keisha and her best friend, Franco, are going on a class trip to the zoo. They sit together on the yellow school bus. At the zoo, they see tigers, camels, and elephants. They look at lions sleeping on rocks, monkeys sitting in trees, and seals swimming in a pond. Franco asks Keisha which animal she likes best. "The zebra," she says, "because he looks like a horse and he has stripes." Franco says, "I like the elephant because she has a very long nose." Keisha and Franco enjoy their day at the zoo.

Turn to page 2.

Check to see that all the children are on the correct page.

Point to the letter S.

Hold up page 2, pointing to the letter S for the children to see.

Look at the picture of a zebra. Now I will read a question. Listen to the question as I read it aloud: Which animal does Keisha say the zebra looks like? Now look at the three pictures in the row under the zebra. Fill in the circle under the correct picture. What is the answer?

Have a child provide the answer.

That's right. The third picture in the row shows a horse. You should have filled in the circle with a <u>c</u> inside.

Check to see that each child has filled in the correct circle.

Does anyone have any questions?

Now I will read the story again. Listen carefully.

Read the story aloud again.

Now point to number 1.

Check to see that all the children are at the correct place.

Now I'm going to read another question. Listen to the question as I read it aloud: Which picture shows something that Keisha and Franco might really do together during their day at the zoo? Look at the three pictures in this row. Fill in the circle under the picture that shows something that might really happen.

Listening Comprehension
High-Frequency Words

Turn to page 3.

Check to see that all the children are on the correct page.

Point to number 2.

Check to see that all the children are at the correct place.

Look at the first word in this row. Now look at the other three words in the row. Fill in the circle under the word that is the same as the first word in the row.

Comprehension
Compare and Contrast

Point to number 3.

Check to see that all the children are at the correct place.

Giraffes have very long necks. Which other part of the giraffe is also very long? Fill in the circle under the picture that shows the answer to the question.

Turn to page 4.

Check to see that all the children are on the correct page.

Point to number 4.

Check to see that all the children are at the correct place.

Look at the two placemats. Now look at the three pictures under the placemats. Fill in the circle under the item that is on both placemats.

Point to number 5.

Check to see that all the children are at the correct place.

Look at the basket. Now look at the three pictures under the basket. Fill in the circle under the item that is in the basket.

Comprehension

Distinguish Between Fantasy and Reality; Classify and Categorize

Turn to page 5.

Check to see that all the children are on the correct page.

Point to number 6.

Check to see that all the children are at the correct place.

Look at the pictures in this row. Fill in the circle under the picture that shows something that is real.

Point to number 7.

Check to see that all the children are at the correct place.

Now look at the pictures in this row. Fill in the circle under the picture that does not belong.

High-Frequency Words

she, he, has, look

Turn to page 6.

Check to see that all the children are on the correct page.

Point to the letter S.

Check to see that all the children are at the correct place. Write the first word from row S on the board followed by the three word choices with their answer circles (a,b,c). Hold up page 7, pointing to the first word in the row so the children can see.

Look at the first word in the row. What is the word? That's right, the word is <u>here</u>. Look at the other three words in the row. I am going to fill in the circle under the word where I see it in the same row.

Fill in the circle <u>c</u> under the word <u>here</u> on the board.

The circle I filled in is <u>c</u> under the word <u>here</u>. It is the same as the first word in the row. Now you will do the same on your paper. Look at the first word in row S. Now fill in the circle under the word where you see it in the same row.

Check to see that all the children have filled in the circle <u>c</u> under the word <u>here</u> in row S.

Does anyone have any questions?

We will continue in the same way. Follow the same instructions for the next four rows. Look at the first word in each row. Then fill in the circle under the word where you see it in the same row.

Phonemic Awareness

Phoneme Isolation

Turn to page 7.

Check to see that all the children are on the correct page.

Point to the letter S.

Hold up page 7, pointing to the first row for all the children to see. Check to see that all the children are at the correct place.

I will say a word: <u>win</u>, /w/ /i/ /n/. What is the beginning sound in /w/ /i/ /n/? Listen to these answer choices: <u>tiger</u>, <u>wagon</u>, <u>owl</u>. Which answer choice has the same beginning sound as /w/ /i/ /n/? That's right. The word <u>wagon</u> has the same beginning sound as /w/ /i/ /n/. Fill in the circle under the picture of the <u>wagon</u> because it has the same beginning sound as /w/ /i/ /n/.

Check to see that all the children have filled in the circle <u>b</u> under the picture of the <u>wagon</u> in row S.

Does anyone have any questions?

Now point to number 12.

Check to see that all the children are at the correct place.

Look at question 12. I will say a word: <u>gift</u>, /g/ /i/ /f/ /t/. What is the beginning sound in /g/ /i/ /f/ /t/? Listen to these answer choices: <u>guitar</u>, <u>fish</u>, <u>toothbrush</u>. Fill in the circle under the picture that has the same beginning sound as /g/ /i/ /f/ /t/.

Now point to number 13.

Check to see that all the children are at the correct place.

Look at question 13. I will say a word: <u>vet</u>, /v/ /e/ /t/. What is the beginning sound in /v/ /e/ /t/? Listen to these answer choices: <u>cave</u>, <u>vase</u>, <u>shell</u>. Fill in the circle under the picture that has the same beginning sound as /v/ /e/ /t/.

Phonemic Awareness
Phoneme Blending

Turn to page 8.
Check to see that all the children are on the correct page.

Point to number 14.
Check to see that all the children are at the correct place.

Look at question 14. I will say a word in parts: /w/ /e/ /b/. What word do you make when you put these sounds together? Listen to these answer choices: <u>bell</u>, <u>web</u>, <u>hen</u>. *Fill in the circle under the picture that has the same sounds as /w/ /e/ /b/.*

Now point to number 15.
Check to see that all the children are at the correct place.

Look at question 15. I will say a word in parts: /f/ /i/ /x/. What word do you make when you put these sounds together? Listen to these answer choices: <u>fix</u>, <u>mix</u>, <u>kick</u>. *Fill in the circle under the picture that has the same sounds as /f/ /i/ /x/.*

Phonemic Awareness
Phoneme Segmentation

Turn to page 9.
Check to see that all the children are on the correct page.

Point to number 16.
Check to see that all the children are at the correct place.

Look at question 16. Listen while I say the sounds in the word <u>great</u>: */g/ /r/ /ā/ /t/. How many sounds do you hear in the word /g/ /r/ /ā/ /t/? Say the word slowly. Fill in the circle under the picture that shows how many sounds you hear in /g/ /r/ /ā/ /t/.*

Point to number 17.
Check to see that all the children are at the correct place.

Look at question 17. Listen while I say the sounds in the word <u>went</u>: */w/ /e/ /n/ /t/. How many sounds do you hear in the word /w/ /e/ /n/ /t/? Say the word slowly. Fill in the circle under the picture that shows how many sounds you hear in /w/ /e/ /n/ /t/.*

Point to number 18.
Check to see that all the children are at the correct place.

Look at question 18. Listen while I say the sounds in the word <u>very</u>: */v/ /e/ /r/ /ē/. How many sounds do you hear in the word /v/ /e/ /r/ /ē/? Say the word slowly. Fill in the circle under the picture that shows how many sounds you hear in /v/ /e/ /r/ /ē/.*

Phonics
Initial /w/w, /v/v

Turn to page 10.
Check to see that all the children are on the correct page.

Point to the letter S in the first row.
Check to see that all the children are at the correct place. Hold up page 10, pointing to the picture of the glove in the first row.

Say the name of the picture. That's right, it is a picture of a <u>glove</u>. *What beginning sound did you hear? Did you hear the /g/ sound in* <u>glove</u>? *Fill in the circle under the letter g.*
Check to see that each child filled in the correct circle.

Does anyone have any questions?

We will continue in the same way on this page for number 16 and number 17.

Point to number 19.
Check to see that all the children are at the correct place.

Say the name of the picture. Then fill in the circle under the letter for the sound that you hear at the beginning of the picture name.

Point to number 20.
Check to see that all the children are at the correct place.

Say the name of the picture. Then fill in the circle under the letter for the sound that you hear at the beginning of the picture name.

Phonics
Final /g/g, /ks/x

Turn to page 11.
Check to see that all the children are on the correct page.

Point to number 21.
Check to see that all the children are at the correct place.

Now we are going to listen for the sound at the end of the word. Say the name of the picture. Then fill in the circle under the letter for the sound that you hear at the end of the picture name.

Now point to number 22.

Check to see that all the children are at the correct place.

We will continue in the same way for number 22. Say the name of the picture. Then fill in the circle under the letter for the sound that you hear at the end of the picture name.

Phonics

Word Families -ox, -en

Turn to page 12.

Check to see that all the children are on the correct page.

Point to number 23.

Check to see that all the children are at the correct place.

Look at the three pictures in this row. Two pictures end with the same sound. The other picture does not belong. Say the name of each picture. Listen for the sound at the end of each word. Then fill in the circle under the picture that does not belong.

Point to number 24.

Check to see that all the children are at the correct place.

Look at the three pictures in this row. Two pictures end with the same sound. The other picture does not belong. Say the name of each picture. Listen for the sound at the end of each word. Then fill in the circle under the picture that does not belong.

Concept Words

Opposites: Big/Small

Turn to page 13.

Check to see that all the children are on the correct page.

Point to the letter S.

Check to see that all the children are at the correct place.

Look at the three pictures. Fill in the circle below the picture that shows a <u>big</u> dog and a <u>small</u> cat. What is the answer? That's right, the second picture shows a <u>big</u> dog and a <u>small</u> cat. The first picture is not the correct answer because it shows a big cat and a small dog. The third picture is also not correct because it shows a cat and a dog that are the same size. You should have filled in the circle with a <u>b</u> inside because that is the picture that shows a <u>big</u> dog and a <u>small</u> cat.

Check to see that each child has filled in the circle with a <u>b</u> inside.

Does anyone have any questions?

Point to number 25.

Check to see that all the children are at the correct place.

We will continue in the same way. Look at the three pictures. Fill in the circle below the picture of the <u>big</u> clock and the <u>small</u> book.

Concept Words

Opposites: Short/Tall, Thin/Fat

Turn to page 14.

Check to see that all the children are on the correct page.

Point to number 26.

Check to see that all the children are at the correct place.

We will continue in the same way as on the previous page. Look at the three pictures. Fill in the circle below the picture of the <u>short</u> boy and the <u>tall</u> girl.

Point to number 27.

Check to see that all the children are at the correct place.

Look at the three pictures. Fill in the circle below the picture of the <u>thin</u> bear and the <u>fat</u> clown.

Name _____

Date _____

Unit Assessment

TESTED SKILLS AND STRATEGIES

- Listening Comprehension
- Comprehension
- High-Frequency Words
- Phonemic Awareness
- Phonics
- Concept Words

Macmillan McGraw-Hill

Name _____

S.

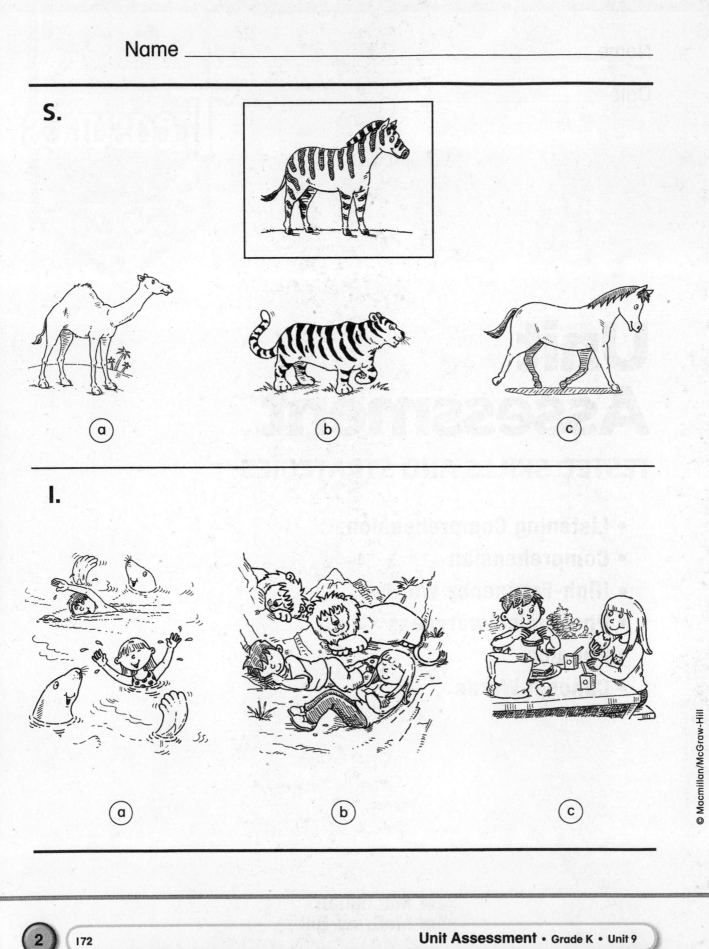

a   b   c

I.

a   b   c

Name ____________________

2.

she	she	see	said
	ⓐ	ⓑ	ⓒ

3.

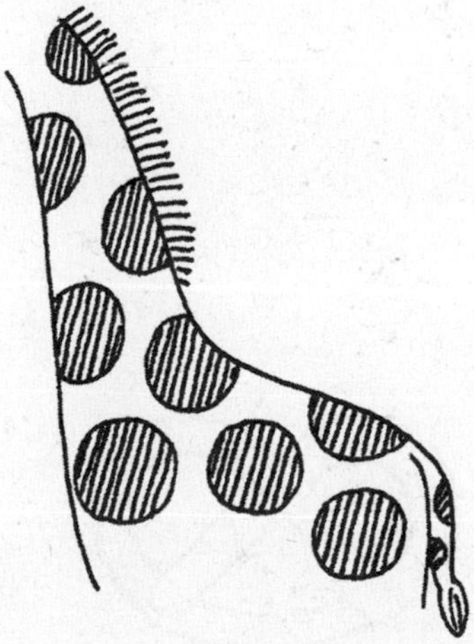
ⓐ

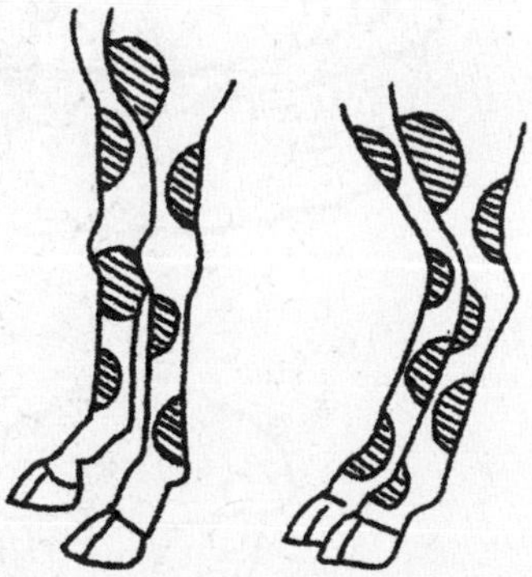
ⓑ

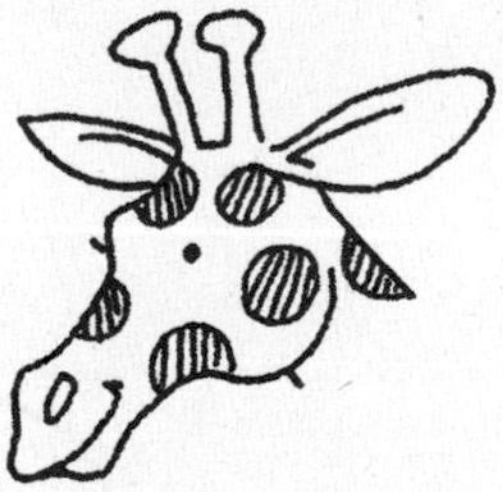
ⓒ

4.

ⓐ   ⓑ   ⓒ

5.

ⓐ   ⓑ   ⓒ

6.

(a) (b) (c)

7.

(a) (b) (c)

Name _____

S.

here	have	are	here
	ⓐ	ⓑ	ⓒ

8.

she	she	the	see
	ⓐ	ⓑ	ⓒ

9.

he	the	we	he
	ⓐ	ⓑ	ⓒ

10.

has	here	has	have
	ⓐ	ⓑ	ⓒ

11.

look	like	little	look
	ⓐ	ⓑ	ⓒ

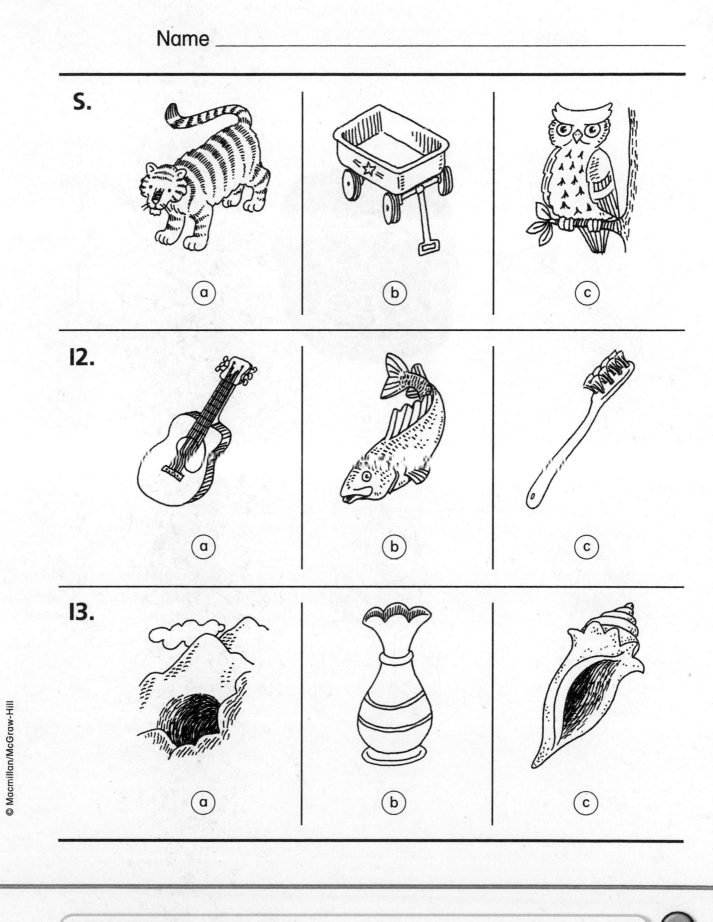

S. a   b   c

12. a   b   c

13. a   b   c

Name _____

14.

ⓐ   ⓑ   ⓒ

15.

ⓐ   ⓑ   ⓒ

Name _____

16.

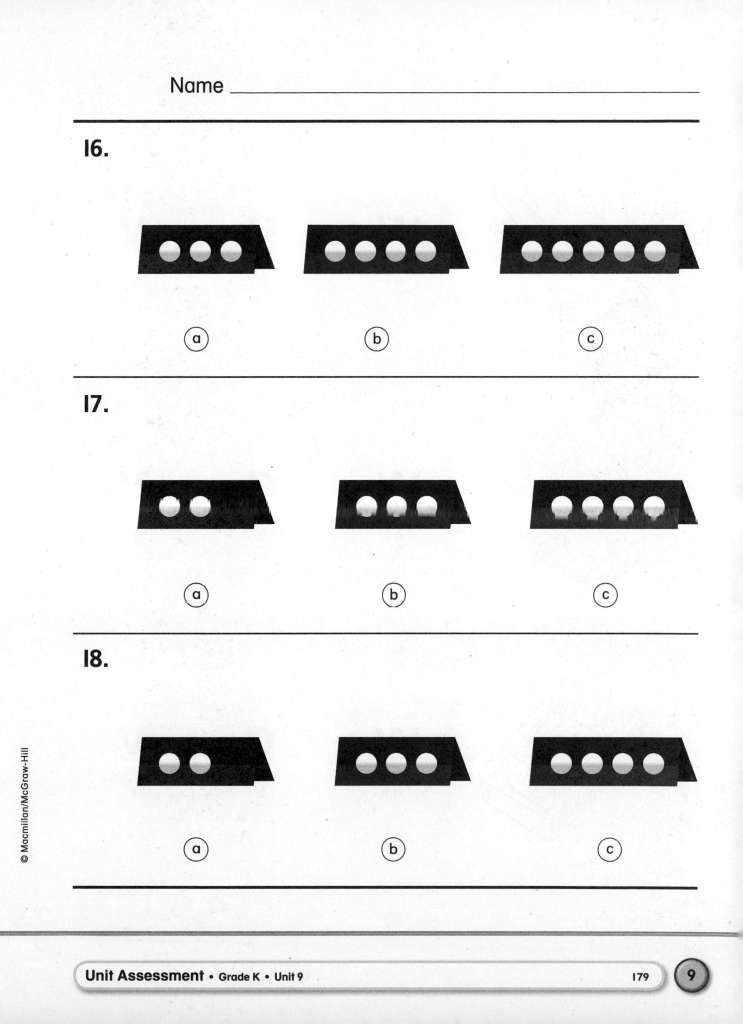

Name _____

S.

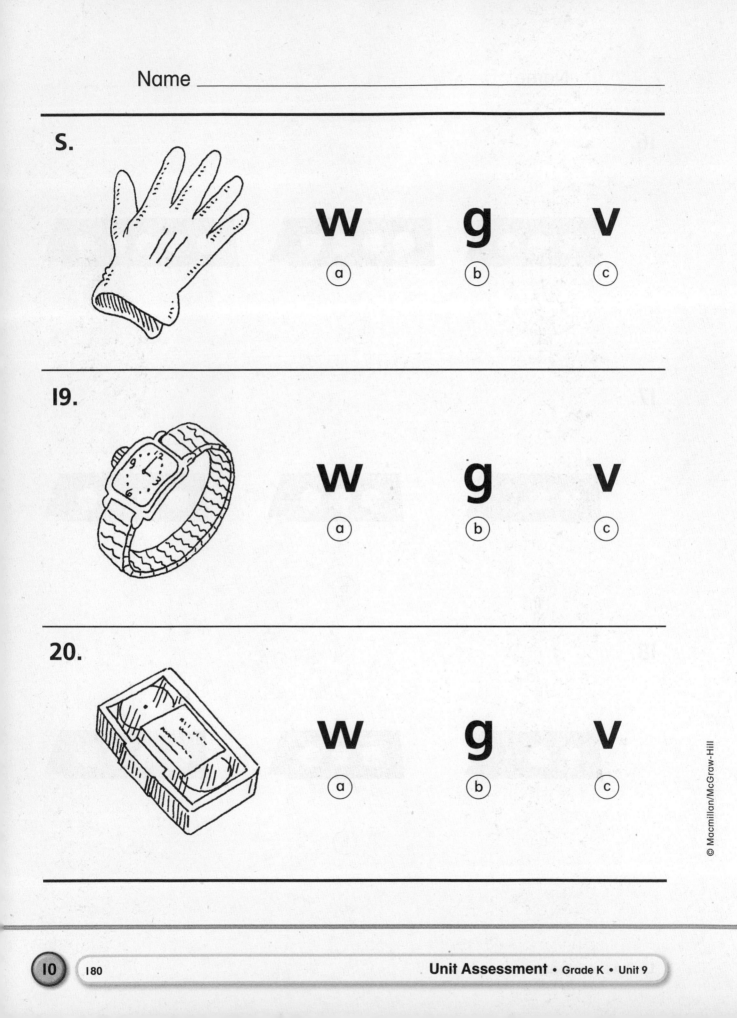

w   g   v
ⓐ   ⓑ   ⓒ

I9.

w   g   v
ⓐ   ⓑ   ⓒ

20.

w   g   v
ⓐ   ⓑ   ⓒ

21.

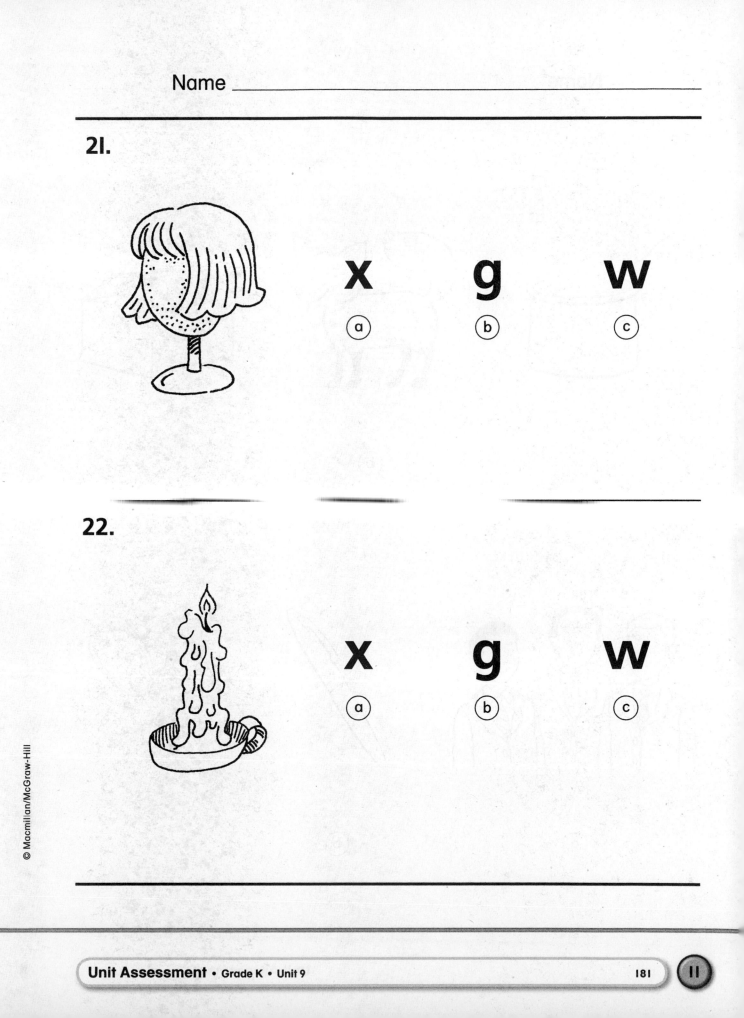

x

(a)

g

(b)

w

(c)

22.

x

(a)

g

(b)

w

(c)

23.

   (a)   (b)   (c)

24.

   (a)   (b)   (c)

Name _____

S.

ⓐ   ⓑ   ⓒ

25.

ⓐ   ⓑ   ⓒ

26.

ⓐ   ⓑ   ⓒ

27.

ⓐ   ⓑ   ⓒ

Name _____

Student Evaluation Chart

TESTED SKILLS	Number Correct	Percent Correct
Listening Comprehension	/2	%
Distinguish between fantasy and reality, 1		
High-frequency word, 3		
Comprehension	/5	%
Compare and contrast, 3, 4, 5		
Distinguish between fantasy and reality, 6		
Classify and categorize, 7		
High Frequency Words	/4	%
she, 8		
he, 9		
has, 10		
look, 11		
Phonemic Awareness	/7	%
Phoneme isolation, 12, 13		
Phoneme blending, 14, 15		
Phoneme segmentation, 16, 17, 18		
Phonics	/6	%
Initial /w/w, 19		
Initial /v/v, 20		
Final /g/g, 21		
Final /ks/x, 22		
Word families -ox, -en, 23, 24		
Concept Words	/3	%
Opposites: big/small, short/tall, thin/fat, 25, 26, 27		
Total Unit Test Score	/27	%

Listening Comprehension
Use Illustrations

You are going to hear a story. After I read the story, I will ask you a few questions. Listen carefully. We will begin now.

Up and Down

When I yawn, my jaw goes down and up, like a yo-yo. When I jump, my body goes up and then down, like a jack-in-the-box. When a jet zooms up to the sky, it must zoom back down again, like a zipper going up and down on a jacket. If you juggle three balls or play with a ball and jacks, where do the balls go? First they go up, and then they come down. What goes up must come down.

Turn to page 3.
Check to see that all the children are on the correct page.

Look at the picture at the top of the page. This picture shows many of the things talked about in the story. You will use this picture to answer the questions on this page.

Point to the letter S.
Hold up page 3, pointing to the letter S for the children to see.

Listen carefully as I tell you something about the picture. Abdul is wearing something that is talked about in the story. Now I will read a question. Listen to the question as I read it aloud: Which of the three pictures in this row is a picture of Abdul? Fill in the circle under the correct picture. What is the answer?
Have a child provide the answer.

That's right. The second picture in the row shows a boy wearing a jacket with a zipper. You should have filled in the circle with a <u>b</u> inside.
Check to see that each child has filled in the correct circle.

Does anyone have any questions?

Now I will read the story again. Listen carefully.
Read the story aloud again.

Now point to number 1.
Check to see that all the children are at the correct place.

Listen carefully as I tell you something about the picture at the top of the page. Jill is playing with something that is talked about in the story. Now I'm going to read another question. Listen to the question as I read it aloud: Which of the three pictures in this row is a picture of Jill? Fill in the circle under the picture that is a picture of Jill.

Listening Comprehension
Identify Cause and Effect; High-Frequency Word

Turn to page 4.
Check to see that all the children are on the correct page.

Point to number 2.
Check to see that all the children are at the correct place.

Listen to the question as I read it aloud: What happens to a baseball that is tossed straight up in the air? Fill in the circle under the picture that shows the answer to the question.

Point to number 3.
Check to see that all the children are at the correct place.

Look at the first word in this row. Now look at the other three words in the row. Fill in the circle under the word that is the same as the first word in the row.

Comprehension
Use Illustrations

Turn to page 5.
Check to see that all the children are on the correct page.

Look at the big picture at the top of this page.
Check to see that all the children are looking at the correct picture.

Point to number 4.
Check to see that all the children are at the correct place.

*I am going to tell you something about the big picture.
Listen carefully and look at the picture. Jin is reading
a storybook. Look at the pictures in number 4 and fill
in the circle under the picture of Jin.*

Point to number 5.

Check to see that all the children are at the correct place.

*I am going to ask you a question about the big picture.
Listen carefully and look at the picture. What is the
girl with the long hair doing? Look at the pictures in
number 5 and fill in the circle under the picture that
shows what the girl is doing.*

Comprehension

Identify Cause and Effect; Identify Setting

Turn to page 6.

Check to see that all the children are on the correct page.

Point to number 6.

Check to see that all the children are at the correct place.

*Look at the picture above the three answer choices.
Now look at the three answer choices. Fill in the circle
under the picture that shows what will happen next.*

Point to number 7.

Check to see that all the children are at the correct place.

*Look at the three pictures in this row. Fill in the circle
under the picture that shows where a farmer belongs.*

High-Frequency Words

with, my, me, where

Turn to page 7.

Check to see that all the children are on the correct page.

Point to the letter S.

**Check to see that all the children are at the correct place.
Write the first word from row S on the board followed by
the three word choices with their answer circles (a,b,c).
Hold up page 7, pointing to the first word in the row so the
children can see.**

*Look at the first word in the row. What is the word?
That's right, the word is <u>has</u>. Look at the other three
words in the row. I am going to fill in the circle under
the word where I see it in the same row.*

Fill in the circle <u>a</u> under the word <u>has</u> on the board.

*The circle I filled in is <u>a</u> under the word <u>has</u>. It is the
same as the first word in the row. Now you will do the
same on your paper. Look at the first word in row S.
Now fill in the circle under the word where you see it
in the same row.*

**Check to see that all the children have filled in the circle
<u>a</u> under the word <u>has</u> in row S.**

Does anyone have any questions?

*We will continue in the same way. Follow the same
instructions for the next four rows. Look at the first
word in each row. Then fill in the circle under the
word where you see it in the same row.*

Phonemic Awareness

Phoneme Isolation

Turn to page 8.

Check to see that all the children are on the correct page.

Point to the letter S.

Check to see that all the children are at the correct place.

*I will say a word: <u>jump</u>, /j/ /u/ /m/ /p/. What is the
beginning sound in /j/ /u/ /m/ /p/? Listen to these
answer choices: <u>muffin</u>, <u>jack-o'lantern</u>, <u>puppet</u>.
Which answer choice has the same beginning sound
as /j/ /u/ /m/ /p/? That's right. The word <u>jack-o'-lantern</u>
has the same beginning sound as /j/ /u/ /m/ /p/. Fill
in the circle under the picture of the <u>jack-o'-lantern</u>
because it has the same beginning sound as
/j/ /u/ /m/ /p/.*

**Check to see that all the children have filled in the circle
<u>b</u> under the picture of the <u>jack-o'-lantern</u> in row S.**

Does anyone have any questions?

Now point to number 12.

Check to see that all the children are at the correct place.

Look at question 12. I will say a word: <u>quick</u>, /kw/ /i/ /k/. What is the beginning sound in /kw/ /i/ /k/? Listen to these answer choices: <u>cheese</u>, <u>statue</u>, <u>queen</u>. Fill in the circle under the picture that has the same beginning sound as /kw/ /i/ /k/.

Now point to number 13.
Check to see that all the children are at the correct place.

Look at question 13. I will say a word: <u>yuck</u>, /y/ /u/ /k/. What is the beginning sound in /y/ /u/ /k/? Listen to these answer choices: <u>yarn</u>, <u>starfish</u>, <u>daisy</u>. Fill in the circle under the picture that has the same beginning sound as /y/ /u/ /k/.

Phonemic Awareness
Phoneme Blending

Turn to page 9.
Check to see that all the children are on the correct page.

Point to number 14.
Check to see that all the children are at the correct place.

Look at question 14. I will say a word in parts: /z/ /i/ /p/. What word do you make when you put these sounds together? Listen to these answer choices: <u>zip</u>, <u>sit</u>, <u>pet</u>. Fill in the circle under the picture that has the same sounds as /z/ /i/ /p/.

Now point to number 15.
Check to see that all the children are at the correct place.

Look at question 15. I will say a word in parts: /j/ /u/ /g/. What word do you make when you put these sounds together? Listen to these answer choices: <u>jig</u>, <u>jug</u>, <u>jog</u>. Fill in the circle under the picture that has the same sounds as /j/ /u/ /g/.

Phonics
Initial /j/j, /y/y

Turn to page 10.
Check to see that all the children are on the correct page.

Point to the letter S in the first row.
Check to see that all the children are at the correct place. Hold up page 10, pointing to the picture of the duck quacking in the first row.

What sound does a duck make? Say the name of the sound that the duck in the picture makes. That's right, the duck in the picture makes a <u>quack</u>. What beginning sound did you hear? Did you hear the /kw/ sound in <u>quack</u>? Fill in the circle under the letters <u>qu</u> because those letters make the beginning sound in quack.
Check to see that all the children have filled in the circle <u>b</u> under the letters <u>qu</u>.

Does anyone have any questions?

We will continue in the same way on this page for number 16 and number 17.

Point to number 16.
Check to see that all the children are at the correct place.

Say the name of the picture. Then fill in the circle under the letter for the sound that you hear at the beginning of the picture name.

Now do the same for number 17.

Phonics
Initial /z/z, /kw/qu

Turn to page 11.
Check to see that all the children are on the correct page.

Point to number 18.
Check to see that all the children are at the correct place.

We will continue in the same way for number 18 and 19. Say the name of the picture. Then fill in the circle under the letter for the sound that you hear at the beginning of the picture name.

Now point to number 19.
Check to see that all the children are at the correct place.

Phonics

Word Families -ut, -un

Turn to page 12.
Check to see that all the children are on the correct page.

Point to number 20.
Check to see that all the children are at the correct place.

Look at the three pictures in this row. Two pictures end with the same sound. The other picture does not belong. Say the name of each picture. Listen for the sound at the end of each word. Then fill in the circle under the picture that does not belong.

Point to number 21.
Check to see that all the children are at the correct place.

Look at the three pictures in this row. Two pictures end with the same sound. The other picture does not belong. Say the name of each picture. Listen for the sound at the end of each word. Then fill in the circle under the picture that does not belong.

Concept Words

Number Words: Two

Turn to page 13.
Check to see that all the children are on the correct page.

Point to the letter S.
Check to see that all the children are at the correct place.

Look at the three pictures of swing sets. Each swing set has a different number of children on swings. Which picture shows <u>three</u> children on swings? Fill in the circle below the picture that shows <u>three</u> children on swings. What is the answer? That's right, the swing set in the second picture shows <u>three</u> children on swings. You should have filled in the circle with a <u>b</u> inside because it shows <u>three</u> children on swings.
Check to see that each child has filled in the circle with a <u>b</u> inside.

Does anyone have any questions?

Point to number 22.
Check to see that all the children are at the correct place.

We will continue in the same way. Listen for the number word and then fill in the circle below the correct picture. Look at the three pictures of vases in this row. Which picture shows <u>two</u> flowers in a vase? Fill in the circle below the picture that shows <u>two</u> flowers in a vase.

Does anyone have any questions?

Concept Words

Number Words: Four, Five

Turn to page 14.
Check to see that all the children are on the correct page.

Point to number 23.
Check to see that all the children are at the correct place.

We will follow the same instructions as on the previous page. Listen for the number word and then fill in the circle below the correct picture. Look at the three pictures of kittens. Which picture shows <u>four</u> kittens? Fill in the circle below the picture of <u>four</u> kittens

Point to number 24.
Check to see that all the children are at the correct place.

Look at the three pictures of birthday cakes in this row. Which picture shows a birthday cake with <u>five</u> candles on it? Fill in the circle below the picture of the birthday cake with <u>five</u> candles on it.

Name _____

Date _____

Treasures

Unit Assessment

TESTED SKILLS AND STRATEGIES

- **Listening Comprehension**
- **Comprehension**
- **High-Frequency Words**
- **Phonemic Awareness**
- **Phonics**
- **Concept Words**

Mc Graw Hill **Macmillan McGraw-Hill**

S.

     (a)   (b)   (c)

I.

     (a)   (b)   (c)

2.

(a)   (b)   (c)

3.

my | me   my   we

(a)   (b)   (c)

Name _____

4.   ⓐ   ⓑ   ⓒ

5.   ⓐ   ⓑ   ⓒ

6.

ⓐ   ⓑ   ⓒ

7.

ⓐ   ⓑ   ⓒ

© Macmillan/McGraw-Hill

Name _____

S.

has | has   was   have
ⓐ   ⓑ   ⓒ

8.

with | was   what   with
ⓐ   ⓑ   ⓒ

9.

my | you   my   go
ⓐ   ⓑ   ⓒ

10.

me | me   we   here
ⓐ   ⓑ   ⓒ

11.

where | he   where   what
ⓐ   ⓑ   ⓒ

S.

a   b   c

12.

a   b   c

13.

a   b   c

Name _____

14.

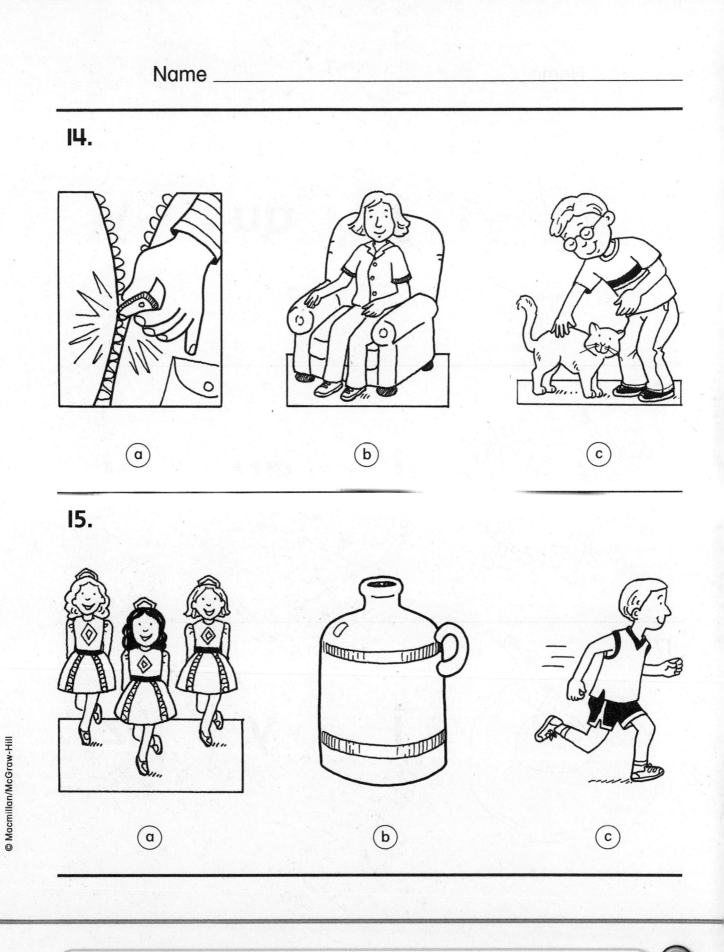

     (a)   (b)   (c)

15.

     (a)   (b)   (c)

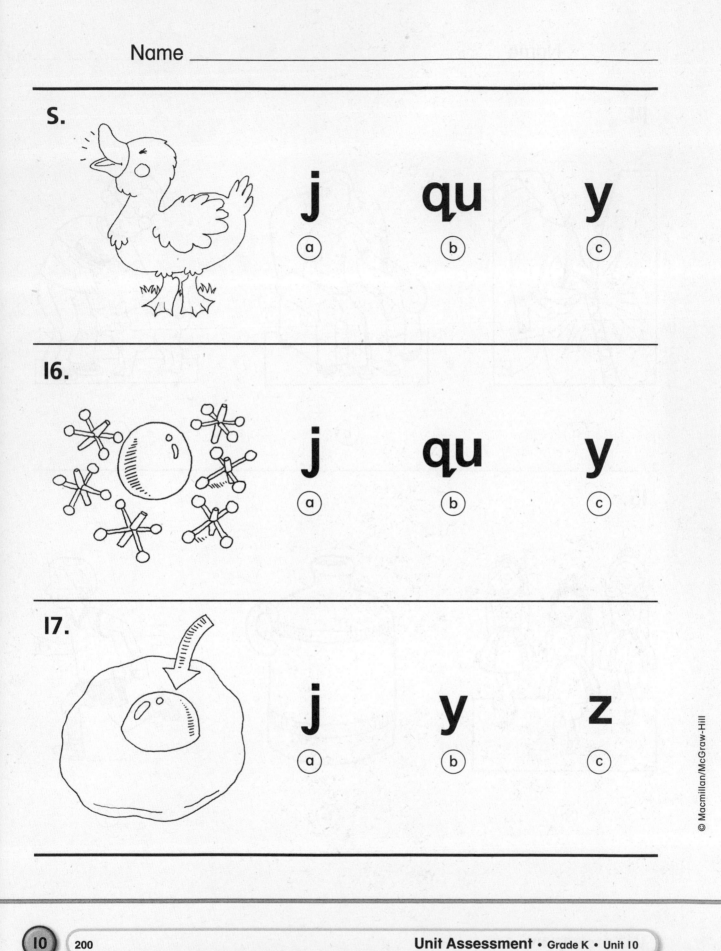

S.

j   qu   y

ⓐ   ⓑ   ©

16.

j   qu   y

ⓐ   ⓑ   ©

17.

j   y   z

ⓐ   ⓑ   ©

Name _____

18.

j   y   z

(a)   (b)   (c)

19.

j   z   qu

(a)   (b)   (c)

20.

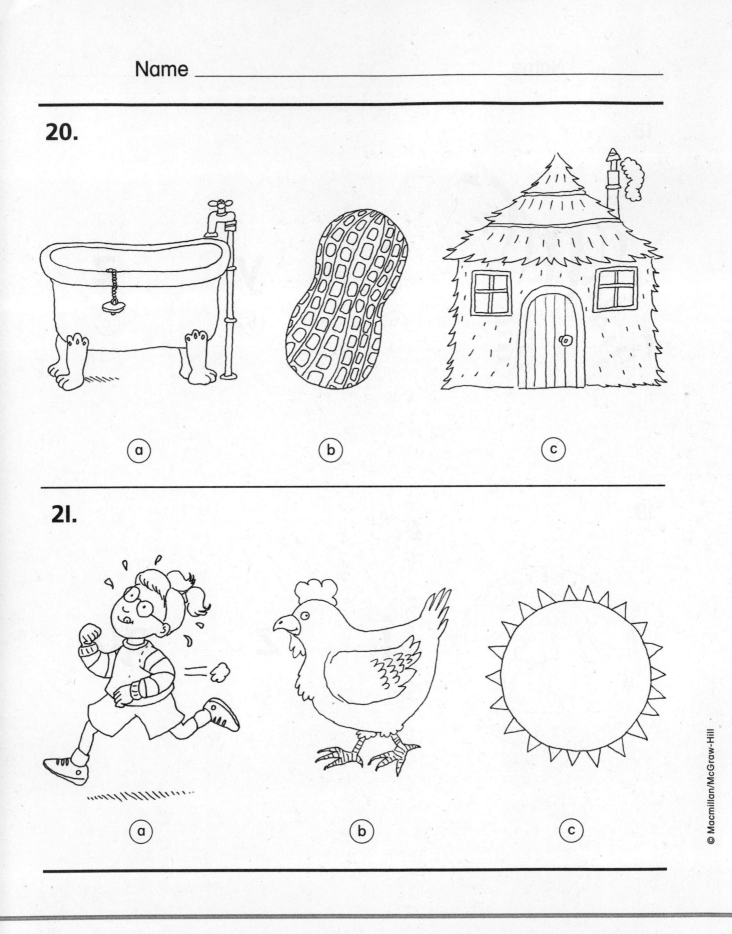

ⓐ   ⓑ   ⓒ

21.

ⓐ   ⓑ   ⓒ

Name _____

S.

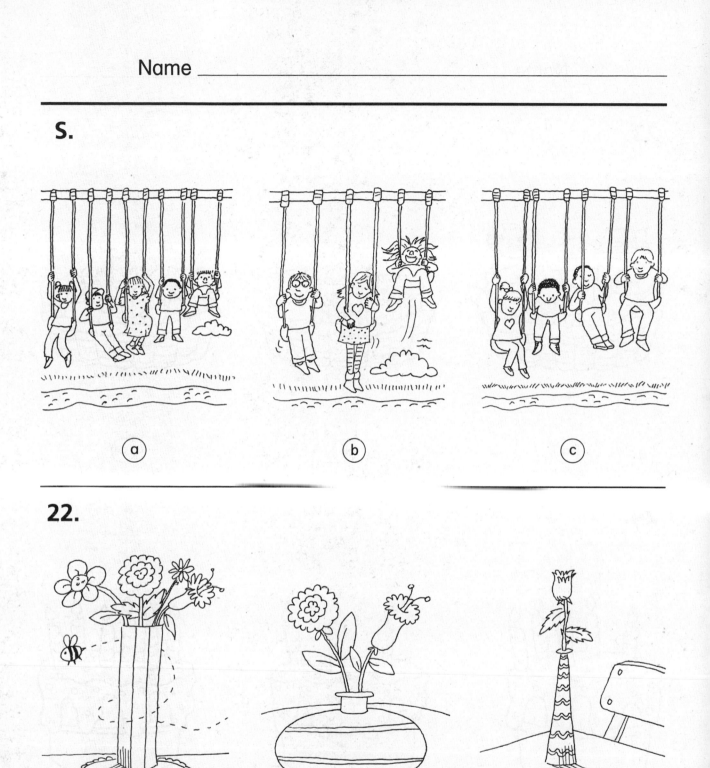

a   b   c

22.

a   b   c

23.

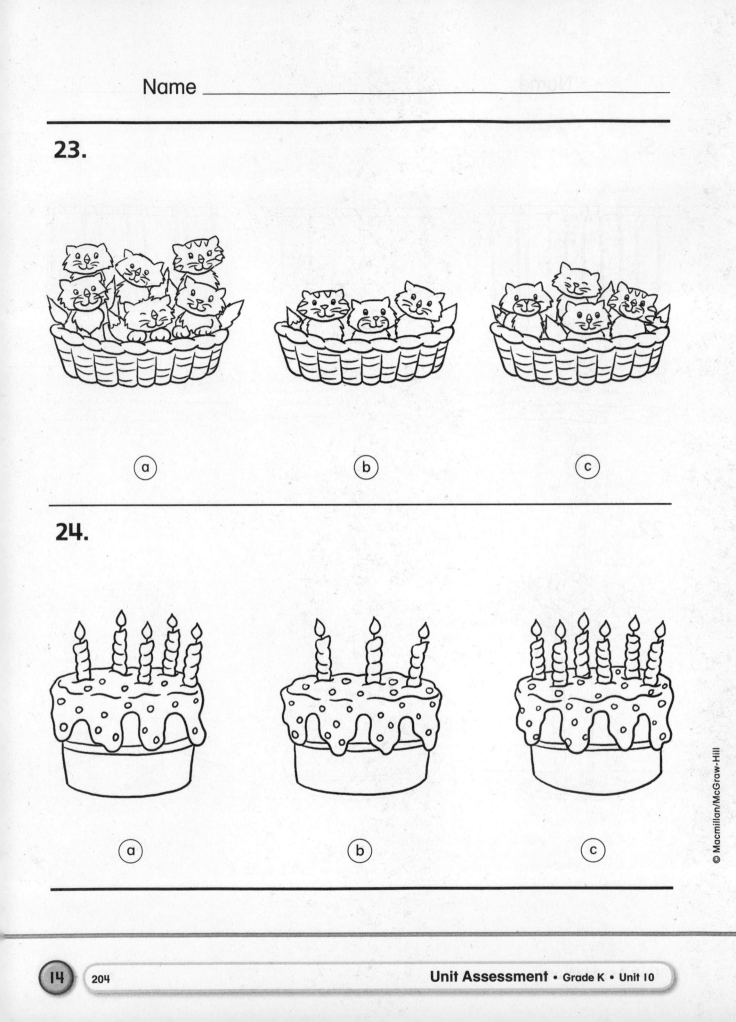

ⓐ　　　　　ⓑ　　　　　ⓒ

24.

ⓐ　　　　　ⓑ　　　　　ⓒ

Kindergarten • Unit 10

Student Evaluation Chart

TESTED SKILLS	Number Correct	Percent Correct
Listening Comprehension	/3	%
Use illustrations, 1		
Identify cause and effect, 2		
High-frequency word, 3		
Comprehension	/4	%
Use illustrations, 4, 5		
Identify cause and effect, 6		
Identify setting, 7		
High Frequency Words	/4	%
with, 8		
my, 9		
me, 10		
where, 11		
Phonemic Awareness	/4	%
Phoneme isolation, 12, 13		
Phoneme blending, 14, 15		
Phonics	/6	%
Initial /j/j, 16		
Initial /y/y, 17		
Initial /z/z, 18		
Initial /kw/qu, 19		
Word families -ut, -un, 20, 21		
Concept Words	/3	%
Number words: two, four, five, 22, 23, 24		
Total Unit Test Score	/24	%

© Macmillan/McGraw-Hill

Listening Comprehension

Identify Character

You are going to hear a story. After I read the story, I will ask you a few questions. Listen carefully. We will begin now.

Jack's Birthday

It is Jack's birthday. His party is at the park next to his house. It is a hot summer day. There is a wading pool at the park. Everyone brings bathing suits and towels. They play tag in the water. Jack floats on his back. Jack's friend Tom does a flip under the water. Then it is time for cake. Jack's father takes the cake out of its box and puts it on a picnic table. Jack's mother lights the candles. Jack makes a wish. He hopes his next birthday party is as much fun as this one. Then he blows out the candles.

Turn to the first page with a picture of an alligator on it.

Check to see that all the children are on the correct page.

Point to the picture of the apple and the letter S.

Hold up page 2, pointing to the apple for the children to see.

I will read a question. Listen to the question as I read it aloud: Where does this story take place? Look at the three pictures in this row. Choose the picture that shows the answer to the question and draw a circle around it. What is the answer?

Have a child provide the answer.

Yes, the first picture in the row shows a park. That is where Jack has his birthday party.

Check to see that each child has drawn a circle around the correct picture.

Does anyone have any questions?

Now I will read the story again. Listen carefully.

Read the story aloud again.

Now point to the picture of the star and the number 1.

Check to see that all the children are at the correct place.

Now I'm going to read another question. Listen to the question as I read it aloud: Who is the main character in this story? Now look at the three pictures in this row. Choose the picture that shows the answer to the question and draw a circle around it.

Listening Comprehension

Identify Sequence of Events; Make and Confirm Predictions

Turn to the page with a picture of a bee on it.

Check to see that all the children are on the correct page.

Point to the picture of the tree and the number 2.

Check to see that all the children are at the correct place.

Now I'm going to read another question. Listen to the question as I read it aloud: What happens first in this story? Now look at the three pictures in this row. Choose the picture that shows the answer to the question and draw a circle around it.

Point to the picture of the fish and the number 3.

Check to see that all the children are at the correct place.

Now I'm going to read another question. Listen to the question as I read it aloud: What will happen right after Jack blows out the candles on his cake? Now look at the three pictures in this row. Choose the picture that shows the answer to the question and draw a circle around it.

Comprehension

Make Inferences, Identify Cause and Effect

Turn to the page with a picture of a cat on it.

Check to see that all the children are on the correct page.

Point to the picture of the apple and the number 4.

Check to see that all the children are at the correct place.

Look at the picture on the left. Then look at the two pictures on the right. Draw a line from the picture on the left to the picture on the right that shows where the person is going.

Now point to the picture of the star and the number 5.

Check to see that all the children are at the correct place.

Now look at the picture on the left. Then look at the two pictures on the right. Draw a line from the picture on the left to the picture on the right that shows what will happen next.

Comprehension

Use Illustrations

Turn to the page with a picture of a dog on it.

Check to see that all the children are on the correct page.

Point to the big picture and the number 6. Now look at the big picture.

Check to see that all children are looking at the correct picture.

I am going to ask you to do something to the picture. Listen carefully and look at the picture. Jim is reading a book. Draw a circle around Jim.

Comprehension

Distinguish Between Fantasy and Reality; Classify and Categorize

Turn to the page with a picture of an alligator on it.

Point to the picture of the flower and the number 7.

Check to see that all the children are at the correct place.

Look at the pictures in this row. Circle the one that shows something that might really happen. Draw a line under the picture that is make-believe.

Point to the picture of the fish and the number 8.

Check to see that all the children are at the correct place.

Look at the pictures in this row. One of the pictures does not belong with the others. Cross out the picture that does not belong.

Comprehension

Compare and Contrast

Turn to the page with a picture of an elephant on it.

Check to see that all the children are on the correct page.

Point to the number 9.

Check to see that all the children are at the correct place.

Look at the two lunch bags at the top of the page. Now look at the picture along the left side of the page. Under each lunch bag, put a check on the line if the lunch has that food. Put an X on the line if the lunch does not have that food.

High-Frequency Words

we, like, see, go, here, was, my, with

Turn to the page with a picture of a frog on it.

Check to see that all the children are on the correct page.

Point to the picture of the apple and the letter S.

Check to see that all the children are at the correct place. Write the four words from row S on the board.

There are four words in this row. Find the word <u>the</u> in this row on your paper. Put your finger on it.

Have a child point to the word <u>the</u> on the board. Draw a circle around the word <u>the</u> on the board.

The word I circled is the word <u>the</u>. It is the word I asked you to find. Draw a circle around the word <u>the</u> on your paper.

Check to see that all the children have circled the correct word.

Does anyone have any questions?

We will continue in the same way. I will name some more words. Find the word I name in each row. Draw a circle around the word. Listen carefully.

Point to the picture of the star and number 10.

Check to see that all the children are at the correct place.

Draw a circle around the word <u>we</u>.

Point to the picture of the tree and number 11.

Check to see that all the children are at the correct place.

Draw a circle around the word <u>like</u>.

Turn to the page with a picture of an elephant on it.

Check to see that all the children are on the correct page.

Point to the picture of the fish and number 12.

Check to see that all the children are at the correct place.

Draw a circle around the word <u>see</u>.

Point to the picture of the flower and number 13.

Check to see that all the children are at the correct place.

Draw a circle around the word <u>go</u>.

Point to the picture of the butterfly and number 14.

Check to see that all the children are at the correct place.

Draw a circle around the word <u>here</u>.

Turn to the page with a picture of a horse.
Make sure children are on the correct page.

Point to the picture of the apple and number 15.
Check to see that all the children are at the correct place.

Draw a circle around the word <u>was</u>.

Point to the picture of the star and number 16.
Check to see that all the children are at the correct place.

Draw a circle around the word <u>my</u>.

Point to the picture of the tree and number 17.
Check to see that all the children are at the correct place.

Draw a circle around the word <u>with</u>.

Phonics
Initial: /s/s, /p/p, /d/d

Turn to the page with a picture of a lizard on it.
Check to see that all the children are on the correct page.

Point to the picture of the apple and the letter S.
Hold up page 11, pointing to apple icon. Check to see that all the children are at the correct place.

Look at the picture of the man. Say <u>man</u>. What beginning sound did you hear? Did you hear the <u>m</u> sound in <u>man</u>? Now write the letter <u>m</u> on the line.
Check to see that all children wrote the correct letter on the correct line.

Does anyone have any questions?

Point to the picture of the star and the number 18.
Check to see that all the children are at the correct place.

Look at the picture. Say the word for the picture. What beginning sound does that word have? Write the letter for the beginning sound on the lines next to the picture.
Now point to the picture of the tree and the number 19.
Check to see that all the children are at the correct place.

Look at the picture. Say the word for the picture. What beginning sound does that word have? Write the letter for the beginning sound on the lines next to the picture.

Now point to the picture of the heart and the number 20.
Check to see that all the children are at the correct place.

Look at the picture. Say the word for the picture. What beginning sound does that word have? Write the letter for the beginning sound on the lines next to the picture.

Phonics
Final: /g/g, /n/n, /t/t

Turn to the page with a picture of a kangaroo on it.
Check to see that all the children are on the correct page.

Point to the picture of the apple and the letter S.
Check to see that all the children are at the correct place.

Say the name of each picture. Which words have the same ending sound as <u>mad</u>? That's right, <u>bed</u> and <u>lid</u> have the same ending sound as <u>mad</u>. They end with the letter <u>d</u>. Draw a circle around the bed and the lid because they have the same ending sound as <u>mad</u>. Now write the letter <u>d</u> on the line.
Check to see that all children circled the correct pictures and wrote the correct letter.

Does anyone have any questions?

Point to the picture of the star and the number 21.

Circle all the pictures that have the same ending sound as the word <u>big</u>. Then write the letter for the ending sound you hear on the line.

Point to the picture of the fish and the number 22.

Circle all the pictures that have the same ending sound as the word <u>fan</u>. Then write the letter for the ending sound you hear on the line.

Point to the picture of the tree and the number 23.

Circle all the pictures that have the same ending sound as the word <u>hat</u>. Then write the letter for the ending sound you hear on the line.

Phonics
Blending: short /u/u, i/i

Turn to the page with a picture of a horse on it.
Check to see that all the children are on the correct page.

Point to the picture of the apple and the letter S.
Check to see that all the children are at the correct place. Hold up page 13, pointing to the picture of the bib in the first row.

Say the name of the picture. That's right. It is a bib.
Now read the two words next to the picture. Draw
a circle around the word that names the picture.
Which word did you circle? That's right. It is the
second word because b-i-b spells bib. *Now write*
the word bib *on the line.*

Check to see that all children circled and wrote the
correct word.

Does anyone have any questions?

Point to the picture of the butterfly and the number 24.
Check to see that all the children are at the correct place.

Circle the word that names the picture. Then write the
word on the line.

Point to the picture of the fish and the number 25.
Check to see that all the children are at the correct place.

Circle the word that names the picture. Then write the
word on the line.

Phonics
Blending: short /o/o, /a/a, /e/e

Turn to the page with a picture of a cat on it.
Check to see that all the children are on the correct page.

Point to the picture of the star and the number 26.
Check to see that all the children are at the correct place.

Circle the word that names the picture. Then write the
word on the line.

Point to the picture of the tree and the number 27.
Check to see that all the children are at the correct place.

Circle the word that names the picture. Then write the
word on the line.

Point to the picture of the heart and the number 28.
Check to see that all the children are at the correct place.

Circle the word that names the picture. Then write the
word on the line.

Name _____

Date _____

Treasures

Benchmark
Assessment

TESTED SKILLS AND STRATEGIES

- Listening Comprehension
- Comprehension
- High-Frequency Words
- Phonics

Macmillan
McGraw-Hill

S.

I.

2.

3.

4.

🍎

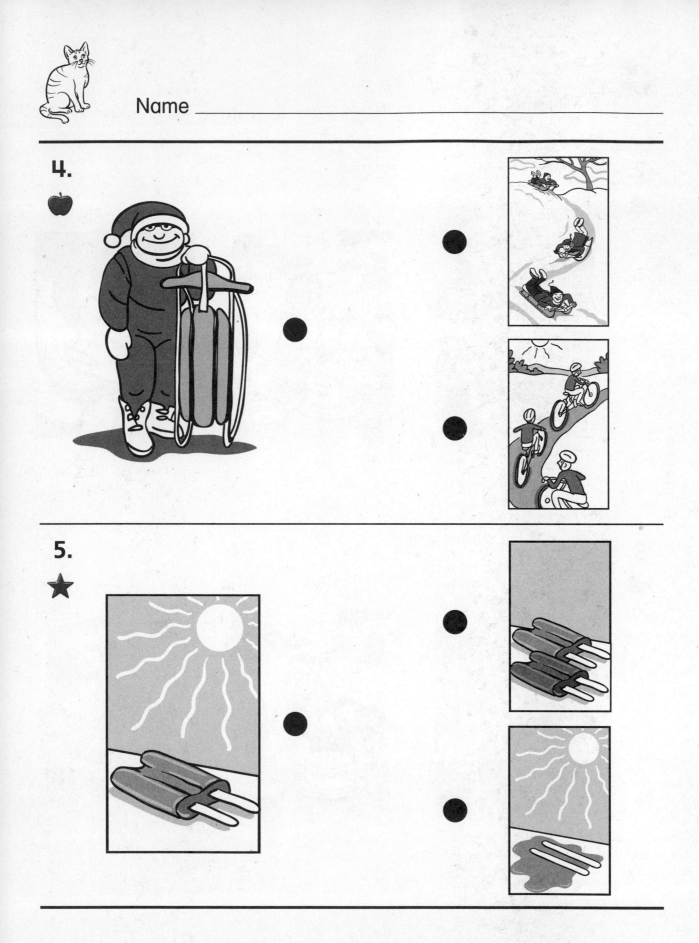

5.

★

Name _____

6.

7.

8.

9.

_____   _____

– – – – – – – – –   – – – – – – – – –

_____   _____

S.

🍎

the	we the see this

10.

⭐

we	we the see is

11.

🌲

like	with like is look

Name _____

12.
🐟

see | he   has   see   this

13.
🍀

go | do   go   to   he

14.
🦋

here | he   like   here   has

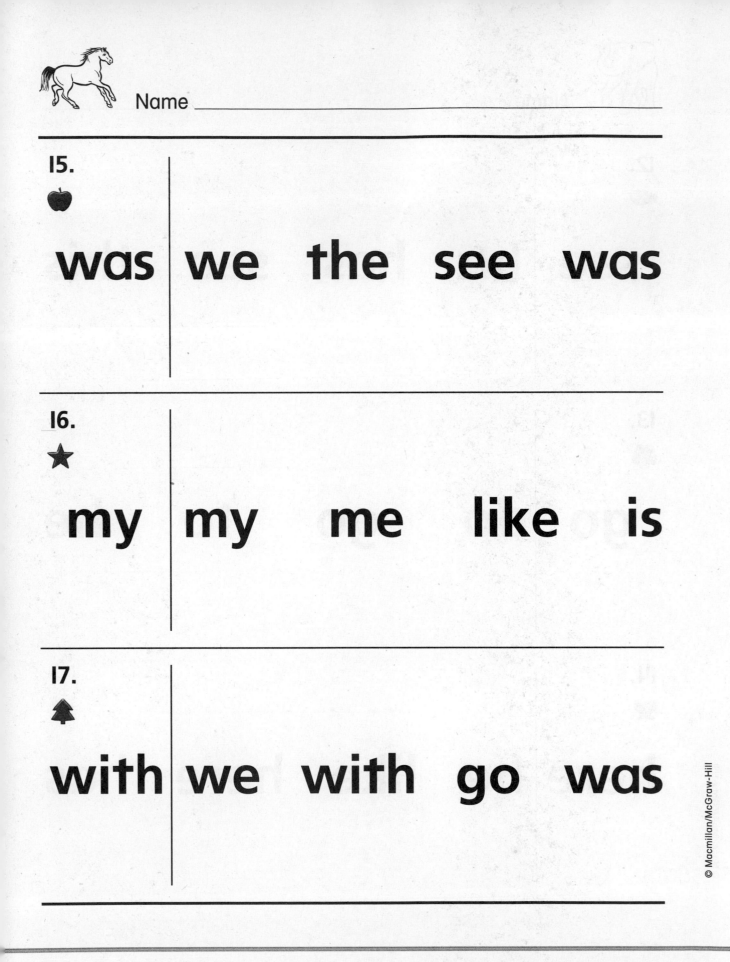

Name _____

15.

🍎 | was | we   the   see   was

16.

⭐ | my | my   me   like   is

17.

🌲 | with | we   with   go   was

Name _____

S.

🍎

_____

- - - - - - - - - - - - - - -

_____

18.

⭐

_____

- - - - - - - - - - - - - - -

_____

19.

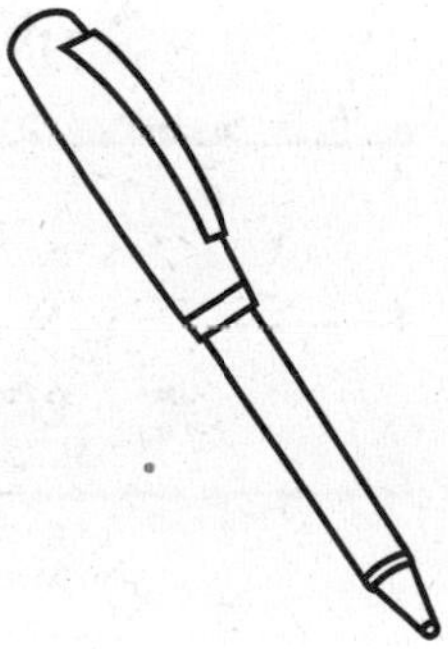

🌲

_____

- - - - - - - - - - - - - - -

_____

20.

❤️

_____

- - - - - - - - - - - - - - -

_____

Name _____

S.

21.

22.

23.

Benchmark Assessment • Grade K • Form A

© Macmillan/McGraw-Hill

S.

job   bib

_____

- - - - - - - - -

_____

24.

fun   tub

_____

- - - - - - - - -

_____

25.

sat   six

_____

- - - - - - - - -

_____

26. ★

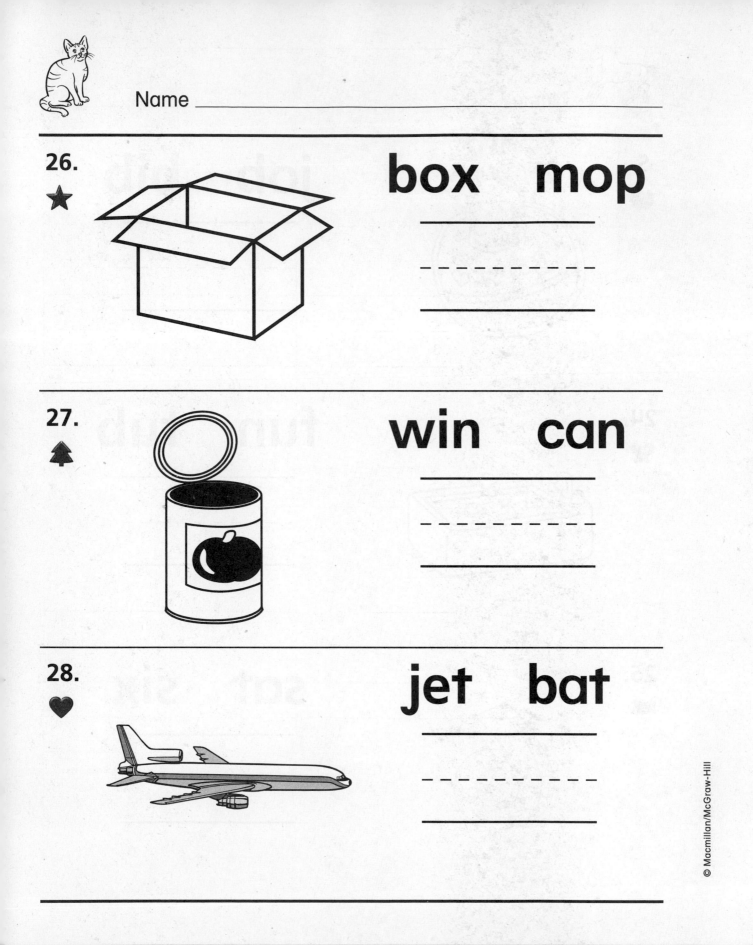

box   mop

_____

- - - - - - - -

_____

27. 🌲

win   can

_____

- - - - - - - -

_____

28. ♥

jet   bat

_____

- - - - - - - -

_____

Name _____

Student Evaluation Chart

TESTED SKILLS	Number Correct	Percent Correct
Listening Comprehension	/3	%
Identify character, 1		
Identify sequence of events, 2		
Make and confirm predictions, 3		
Comprehension	/6	%
Make inferences, 4		
Identify cause and effect, 5		
Use illustrations, 6		
Distinguish between fantasy and reality, 7		
Classify and categorize, 8		
Compare and contrast, 9		
High-Frequency Words	/8	%
we, like, see, go, here, was, my, with, 10–17		
Phonics	/11	%
Initial /s/s, /p/p, /d/d, 18–20		
Final /g/g, /n/n, /t/t, 21–23		
Short /u/u, /i/i, /o/o, /a/a, /e/e, 24–28		
Total Benchmark Test Score	/28	%

Listening Comprehension

Identify Plot

You are going to hear a story. After I read the story, I will ask you a few questions. Listen carefully. We will begin now.

Ann's Dance Shoe

"It's time to go to dance class," said Ann's mother. "Hurry, or we will be late."

"One of my dance shoes is gone," said Ann. She had put both dance shoes near the door of her room. Now, there was only one shoe there.

Ann looked under her bed. She looked in her school bag. Then she saw a dog toy on the floor. She had an idea.

She called the dog. The dog came running. He had the missing shoe in his mouth. Ann gave the dog his toy and took her shoe. Now she was ready to go.

Turn to the first page with a picture of an alligator on it.

Check to see that all the children are on the correct page.

Point to the picture of the apple and the letter S.

Hold up page 2, pointing to the apple for the children to see.

I will read a question. Listen to the question as I read it aloud: Where does this story take place? Look at the three pictures in this row. Choose the picture that shows the answer to the question and draw a circle around it. What is the answer?

Have a child provide the answer.

Yes, the the second picture shows Ann's bedroom. Ann looks for her shoe in her room.

Check to see that each child has drawn a circle around the correct picture.

Does anyone have any questions?

Now I will read the story again. Listen carefully.

Read the story aloud again.

Now point to the picture of the star and the number 1.

Check to see that all the children are at the correct place.

Now I'm going to read another question. Listen to the question as I read it aloud: What is missing at the beginning of the story? Now look at the three pictures in this row. Choose the picture that shows the answer to the question and draw a circle around it.

Listening Comprehension

Identify Sequence of Events; Make and Confirm Predictions

Turn to the page with a picture of a bee on it.

Check to see that all the children are on the correct page.

Point to the picture of the tree and the number 2.

Check to see that all the children are at the correct place.

Now I'm going to read another question. Listen to the question as I read it aloud: What happens last in this story? Now look at the three pictures in this row. Choose the picture that shows the answer to the question and draw a circle around it.

Point to the picture of the fish and the number 3.

Check to see that all the children are at the correct place.

Now I'm going to read another question. Listen to the question as I read it aloud: What will Ann do next? Choose the picture that shows the answer to the question and draw a circle around it.

Comprehension

Make Inferences; Identify Cause and Effect

Turn to the page with a picture of a cat on it.

Check to see that all the children are on the correct page.

Point to the picture of the apple and the number 4.

Check to see that all the children are at the correct place.

Look at the picture on the left. Then look at the two pictures on the right. Draw a circle around the picture that shows where the person is going.

Now point to the picture of the star and the number 5.

Check to see that all the children are at the correct place.

Now look at the picture on the left. Then look at the two pictures on the right. Draw a line from the picture on the left to the picture on the right that shows what will happen next.

Comprehension
Use Illustrations

Turn to the page with a picture of a dog on it.
Check to see that all the children are on the correct page.

Point to the big picture and the number 6. Now look at the big picture.
Check to see that all children are looking at the correct picture.

I am going to ask you to do something to the picture. Listen carefully and look at the picture. Wendy is eating a bowl of cereal. Draw a circle around Wendy.

Comprehension
Distinguish Between Fantasy and Reality; Classify and Categorize

Turn to the page with a picture of an alligator on it.

Point to the picture of the flower and the number 7.
Check to see that all the children are at the correct place.

Look at the pictures in this row. Circle the one that shows something that might really happen. Draw a line under the picture that is make-believe.

Point to the picture of the fish and the number 8.
Check to see that all the children are at the correct place.

Look at the pictures in this row. One of the pictures does not belong with the others. Cross out the picture that does not belong.

Comprehension
Compare and Contrast

Turn to the page with a picture of an elephant on it.
Check to see that all the children are on the correct page.

Point to the number 9.
Check to see that all the children are at the correct place.

Look at the two groups of items at the top of the page. Now look at the picture along the left side of the page. Under each group of items, put a check on the line if the group has that item. Put an X on the line if the group does not have that item.

High-Frequency Words
look, me, where, she, to, and, play, for

Turn to the page with a picture of a frog on it.
Check to see that all the children are on the correct page.

Point to the picture of the apple and the letter S.
Check to see that all the children are at the correct place. Write the four words from row S on the board.

There are four words in this row. Find the word <u>he</u> in this row on your paper. Put your finger on it.
Have a child point to the word <u>he</u> on the board. Draw a circle around the word <u>he</u> on the board.

The word I circled is the word <u>he</u>. It is the word I asked you to find. Draw a circle around the word <u>he</u> on your paper.
Check to see that all the children have circled the correct word.

Does anyone have any questions?

We will continue in the same way. I will name some more words. Find the word I name in each row. Draw a circle around the word. Listen carefully.

Point to the picture of the star and number 10.
Check to see that all the children are at the correct place.

Draw a circle around the word <u>look</u>.

Point to the picture of the tree and number 11.
Check to see that all the children are at the correct place.

Draw a circle around the word <u>me</u>.

Turn to the page with a picture of an elephant on it.
Check to see that all the children are on the correct page.

Point to the picture of the fish and number 12.
Check to see that all the children are at the correct place.

Draw a circle around the word <u>where</u>.

Point to the picture of the flower and number 13.
Check to see that all the children are at the correct place.

Draw a circle around the word <u>she</u>.

Point to the picture of the butterfly and number 14.
Check to see that all the children are at the correct place.

Draw a circle around the word <u>to</u>.

Turn to the page with a picture of a horse on it.
Make sure children are on the correct page.

Point to the picture of the apple and number 15.
Check to see that all the children are at the correct place.

Draw a circle around the word <u>and</u>.

Point to the picture of the star and number 16.
Check to see that all the children are at the correct place.

Draw a circle around the word <u>play</u>.

Point to the picture of the tree and number 17.
Check to see that all the children are at the correct place.

Draw a circle around the word <u>for</u>.

Phonics
Initial: /s/s, /p/p, /d/d

Turn to the page with a picture of a lizard on it.
Check to see that all the children are on the correct page.

Point to the picture of the apple and the letter S.
Hold up page 11, pointing to apple icon. Check to see that all the children are at the correct place.

Look at the picture. Say <u>mop</u>. *What beginning sound did you hear? Did you hear the* <u>m</u> *sound in* <u>mop</u>? *Now write the letter* <u>m</u> *on the line.*
Check to see that all children wrote the correct letter on the correct line.

Does anyone have any questions? We will continue in the same way on this page. Look at each picture. Say the name of each picture. Then write the letter for the beginning sound you hear on the lines.

Point to the picture of the star and the number 18.
Check to see that all the children are at the correct place.

Look at the picture. Say the word for the picture. What beginning sound does that word have? Write the letter for the beginning sound on the line next to the picture.

Now point to the picture of the tree and the number 19. Check to see that all the children are at the correct place.

Look at the picture. What beginning sound does that word have? Write the letter for the beginning sound on the line next to the picture.

Now point to the picture of the heart and the number 20.
Check to see that all the children are at the correct place.

Look at the picture. What beginning sound does that word have? Write the letter for the beginning sound on the line next to the picture.

Phonics
Final: /g/g, /n/n, /t/t

Turn to the page with a picture of a kangaroo on it.
Check to see that all the children are on the correct page.

Point to the picture of the apple and the letter S.
Check to see that all the children are at the correct place.

Say the name of each picture. Which words have the same ending sound as <u>dad</u>? *That's right,* <u>pad</u> *and* <u>pod</u> *have the same ending sound as* <u>dad</u>. *They end with the letter* <u>d</u>. *Draw a circle around the pad and the pod because they have the same ending sound as* <u>dad</u>. *Now write the letter* <u>d</u> *on the line.*
Check to see that all children circled the correct pictures and wrote the correct letter.

Does anyone have any questions?

Point to the picture of the star and the number 21.

Circle all the pictures that have the same ending sound as the word <u>fig</u>. *Then write the letter for the ending sound you hear on the line.*

Point to the picture of the fish and the number 22.

Circle all the pictures that have the same ending sound as the word <u>win</u>. *Then write the letter for the ending sound you hear on the line.*

Point to the picture of the tree and the number 23.

Circle all the pictures that have the same ending sound as the word <u>bit</u>. *Then write the letter for the ending sound you hear on the line.*

Phonics

Blending: short /u/u, /i/i

Turn to the page with a picture of a horse on it.
Check to see that all the children are on the correct page.

Point to the picture of the apple and the letter S.
Check to see that all the children are at the correct place. Hold up page 13, pointing to the picture of the fin in the first row.

Say the name of the picture. That's right. It is a fin. Now read the two words next to the picture. Draw a circle around the word that names the picture. Which word did you circle? That's right. It's the second word because f-i-n spells <u>fin</u>. Now write the word <u>fin</u> on the line.
Check to see that all children circled and wrote the correct word.

Does anyone have any questions?

Point to the picture of the butterfly and the number 24.
Check to see that all the children are at the correct place.

Circle the word that names the picture. Then write the word on the line.

Point to the picture of the fish and the number 25.
Check to see that all the children are at the correct place.

Circle the word that names the picture. Then write the word on the line.

Phonics

Blending: short /o/o, /a/a, /e/e

Turn to the page with a picture of a cat on it.
Check to see that all the children are on the correct page.

Point to the picture of the star and the number 26.
Check to see that all the children are at the correct place.

Circle the word that names the picture. Then write the word on the line.

Point to the picture of the tree and the number 27.
Check to see that all the children are at the correct place.

Circle the word that names the picture. Then write the word on the line.

Point to the picture of the heart and the number 28.
Check to see that all the children are at the correct place.

Circle the word that names the picture. Then write the word on the line.

Name _____

Date _____

Treasures

Benchmark Assessment

TESTED SKILLS AND STRATEGIES

- Listening Comprehension
- Comprehension
- High-Frequency Words
- Phonics

Macmillan
McGraw-Hill

S.

l.

2.

3.

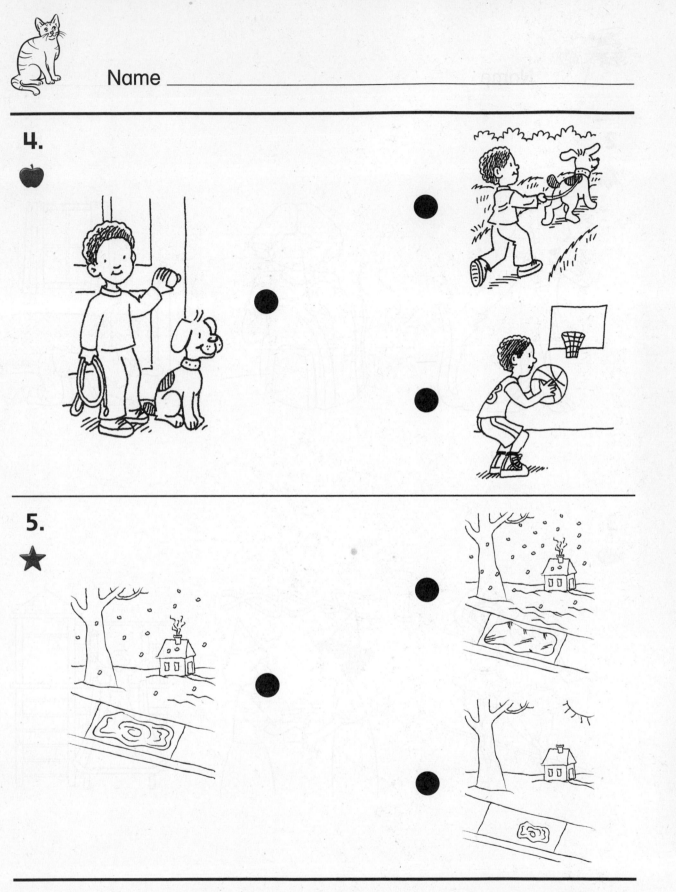

4.

5.

Name _____

6.

7.

8.

Name _____

9.

_____   _____

- - - - - - - - - -   - - - - - - - - - -

_____   _____

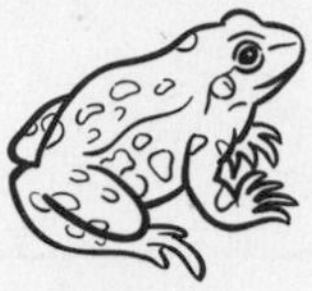

S.

🍎

he | we   the   he   me

10.

★

look | like   look   you   do

11.

🌲

me | we   the   he   me

12.

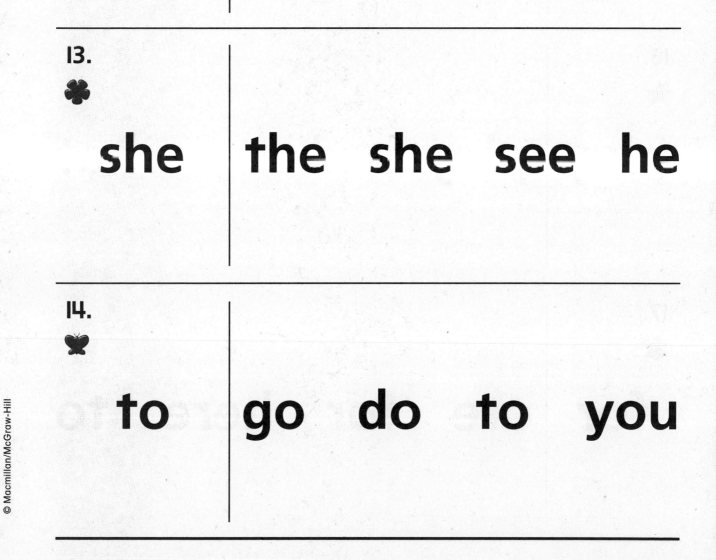

where | we he are where

13.

she | the she see he

14.

to | go do to you

15.

🍎

| and | a | is | and | are |

16.

★

| play | play | and | me | what |

17.

🌲

| for | are | for | here | to |

Benchmark Assessment • Grade K • Form B

Name _____

S.

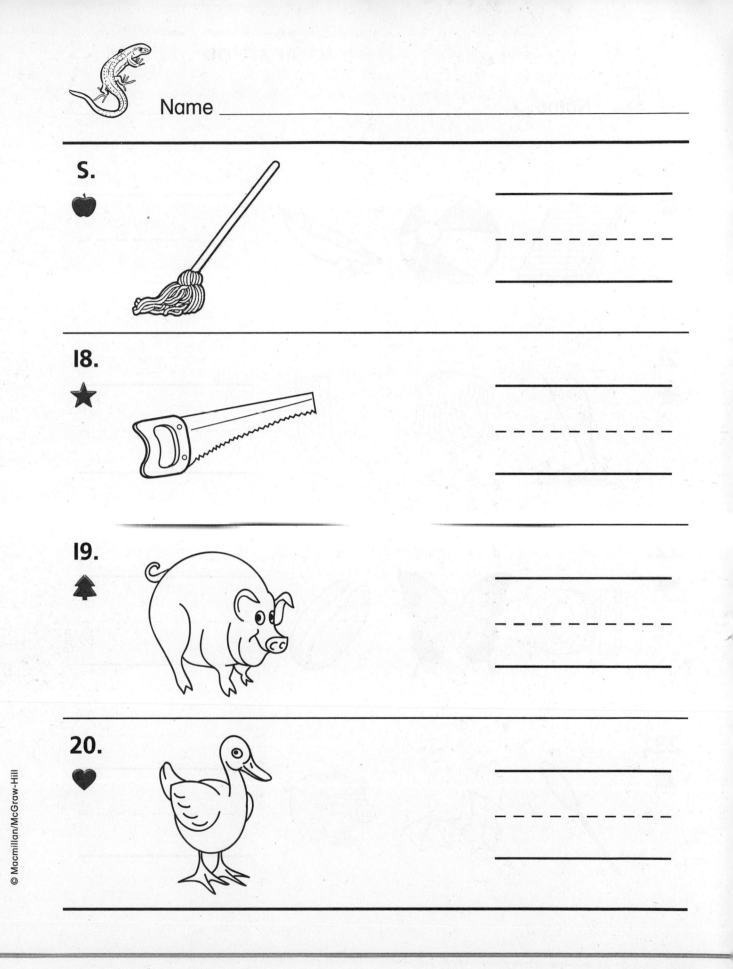

18.

19.

20.

Name _____

S. _____

21. _____

22. _____

23. _____

Name _____

S.

fan   fin

_____

- - - - - - - - -

_____

24.

rag   rug

_____

- - - - - - - - -

_____

25.

lap   lip

_____

- - - - - - - - -

_____

© Macmillan/McGraw-Hill

26. ★

hip   hop

_____

- - - - - - - - - - -

_____

27. 🌲

map   man

_____

- - - - - - - - - - -

_____

28. ♥

bed   bad

_____

- - - - - - - - - - -

_____

Name _____

Kindergarten • Benchmark Assessment • Form B

Student Evaluation Chart

TESTED SKILLS	Number Correct	Percent Correct
Listening Comprehension	/3	%
Identify plot, 1		
Identify sequence of events, 2		
Make and confirm predictions, 3		
Comprehension	/6	%
Make inferences, 4		
Identify cause and effect, 5		
Use illustrations, 6		
Distinguish between fantasy and reality, 7		
Classify and categorize, 8		
Compare and contrast, 9		
High-Frequency Words	/8	%
look, me, where, she, to, and, play, for, 10–17		
Phonics	/11	%
*Initial /s/*s, */p/*p, */d/*d, 18–20		
*Final /g/*g, */n/*n, */t/*t, 21–23		
*Short /u/*u, */i/*i, */o/*o, */a/*a, */e/*e, 24–28		
Total Benchmark Test Score	/28	%

Name _____ Date _____

Answer Sheet

Unit Assessment

1 Ⓐ Ⓑ Ⓒ Ⓓ	10 Ⓐ Ⓑ Ⓒ Ⓓ	19 Ⓐ Ⓑ Ⓒ Ⓓ
2 Ⓐ Ⓑ Ⓒ Ⓓ	11 Ⓐ Ⓑ Ⓒ Ⓓ	20 Ⓐ Ⓑ Ⓒ Ⓓ
3 Ⓐ Ⓑ Ⓒ Ⓓ	12 Ⓐ Ⓑ Ⓒ Ⓓ	21 Ⓐ Ⓑ Ⓒ Ⓓ
4 Ⓐ Ⓑ Ⓒ Ⓓ	13 Ⓐ Ⓑ Ⓒ Ⓓ	22 Ⓐ Ⓑ Ⓒ Ⓓ
5 Ⓐ Ⓑ Ⓒ Ⓓ	14 Ⓐ Ⓑ Ⓒ Ⓓ	23 Ⓐ Ⓑ Ⓒ Ⓓ
6 Ⓐ Ⓑ Ⓒ Ⓓ	15 Ⓐ Ⓑ Ⓒ Ⓓ	24 Ⓐ Ⓑ Ⓒ Ⓓ
7 Ⓐ Ⓑ Ⓒ Ⓓ	16 Ⓐ Ⓑ Ⓒ Ⓓ	25 Ⓐ Ⓑ Ⓒ Ⓓ
8 Ⓐ Ⓑ Ⓒ Ⓓ	17 Ⓐ Ⓑ Ⓒ Ⓓ	26 Ⓐ Ⓑ Ⓒ Ⓓ
9 Ⓐ Ⓑ Ⓒ Ⓓ	18 Ⓐ Ⓑ Ⓒ Ⓓ	27 Ⓐ Ⓑ Ⓒ Ⓓ

Answer Sheet

Benchmark Assessment

1	Ⓐ	Ⓑ	Ⓒ	Ⓓ	11	Ⓐ	Ⓑ	Ⓒ	Ⓓ	21	Ⓐ	Ⓑ	Ⓒ	Ⓓ
2	Ⓐ	Ⓑ	Ⓒ	Ⓓ	12	Ⓐ	Ⓑ	Ⓒ	Ⓓ	22	Ⓐ	Ⓑ	Ⓒ	Ⓓ
3	Ⓐ	Ⓑ	Ⓒ	Ⓓ	13	Ⓐ	Ⓑ	Ⓒ	Ⓓ	23	Ⓐ	Ⓑ	Ⓒ	Ⓓ
4	Ⓐ	Ⓑ	Ⓒ	Ⓓ	14	Ⓐ	Ⓑ	Ⓒ	Ⓓ	24	Ⓐ	Ⓑ	Ⓒ	Ⓓ
5	Ⓐ	Ⓑ	Ⓒ	Ⓓ	15	Ⓐ	Ⓑ	Ⓒ	Ⓓ	25	Ⓐ	Ⓑ	Ⓒ	Ⓓ
6	Ⓐ	Ⓑ	Ⓒ	Ⓓ	16	Ⓐ	Ⓑ	Ⓒ	Ⓓ	26	Ⓐ	Ⓑ	Ⓒ	Ⓓ
7	Ⓐ	Ⓑ	Ⓒ	Ⓓ	17	Ⓐ	Ⓑ	Ⓒ	Ⓓ	27	Ⓐ	Ⓑ	Ⓒ	Ⓓ
8	Ⓐ	Ⓑ	Ⓒ	Ⓓ	18	Ⓐ	Ⓑ	Ⓒ	Ⓓ	28	Ⓐ	Ⓑ	Ⓒ	Ⓓ
9	Ⓐ	Ⓑ	Ⓒ	Ⓓ	19	Ⓐ	Ⓑ	Ⓒ	Ⓓ					
10	Ⓐ	Ⓑ	Ⓒ	Ⓓ	20	Ⓐ	Ⓑ	Ⓒ	Ⓓ					

Scoring Instructions

Using the Student Evaluation Charts

After each Unit and Benchmark Assessment there is a Student Evaluation Chart. It lists all of the skills covered and the number of the question that assesses each skill. Each question is worth one point each.

- In the column labeled "Number Correct," fill in the number of questions answered correctly for each skill. Count the total number of correct responses, and write the number for each subtest above the total possible score.

- Add the scores for each skill (number of items answered correctly) to determine the total test score.

- To convert these raw test scores to percentages, divide the number answered correctly by the total number of questions. Example: A student answers 9 out of 12 items correctly; 9 divided by 12 = .75, or 75%.

Evaluating the Scores

The primary focus of the Unit Assessment is to measure student progress toward mastery of each skill. Scores that fall below the 80th percentile suggest that students require additional instruction before mastery of that skill can be achieved.

Evaluating the results of this assessment provides specific information about students' daily instructional needs. We recommend that you use these results for instructional planning and reteaching opportunities. Compare these results with your own observations of students' work and identify objectives that still need reinforcement. Incorporate these into your instructional plans for the coming unit for individual, small group, or whole group instruction as indicated.

Teacher's Notes

Answer Key Unit Assessments

Unit 1

Items 1–3:
Children will circle the following:

1. playground
2. ice cream cones
3. the
4. Children will draw a line to the rose.
5. Children will draw a line to the car.

Items 6–19:
Children will circle the following:

6. barn
7. beach
8. we
9. the
10. man
11. jam
12. moon
13. fan
14. mask, milk
15. mirror, money
16. ham, comb
17. bat, van
18. cap, pan
19. bat, lamp
20. Children will underline the golf ball and circle the beach ball.
21. Children will underline the toy fire engine and circle the big fire engine.
22. Children will draw an X on the tall building and circle the short building.
23. Children will draw an X on the tall tree and circle the short tree.

Unit 2

Items 1–5:
Children will circle the following:

1. dentist
2. a
3. sink with a hairbrush
4. king
5. sad face
6. ✓, ✗
7. ✓, ✓

Items 8–13:
Children will circle the following:

8. a
9. like
10. seal
11. pig
12. sock
13. pen
14. Children will write *s*.
15. Children will write *s*.
16. Children will write *p*.
17. Children will write *p*.
18. Children will write *m*.
19. Children will write *a*.
20. Children will color the apple red and the grapes yellow.
21. Children will color the corn yellow and the broccoli blue.
22. Children will color the dog blue and the turtle red.

Unit 3

Items 1–13:
Children will circle the following:

1. woman
2. go
3. bag of marbles
4. girl and birthday cake
5. boy and mother planting seeds
6. boy building a sandcastle
7. teddy bear
8. see
9. go
10. top
11. dog's tail
12. tack
13. kick
14. Children will circle the tree and the teeth and they will write *t*.
15. Children will circle the toe and the table and they will write *t*.
16. Children will write *t* and they will circle the nut and the boat.
17. Children will write *i* and they will circle the fish and the mitt.
18. Children will circle *sit* and they will write *sit*.
19. Children will circle *pig* and they will write *pig*.
20. Children will color the gift box and the square yellow.
21. Children will color the balloon and the circle red.
22. Children will color the teepee and the triangle blue.

Unit 4

Items 1–3:
Children will circle the following:

1. hands placing top slice of bread
2. to
3. glass
4. <u>First</u>: children will draw an X over the picture with the mother holding the picnic basket; <u>Next</u>: children will underline the picture with the mother holding an apple in one hand and a sandwich in the other; <u>Last</u>: children will circle the picture with the mother holding an apple core.
5. <u>First</u>: children will draw an X over the picture with the woman holding the stack of dishes; <u>Next</u>: children will underline the picture with the man washing dishes; <u>Last</u>: children will circle the picture with the man and girl walking away.
6. Children will draw a line to the bed.
7. Children will draw a line to the beach scene.

Items 8–13:
Children will circle the following:

8. to
9. have
10. nest
11. cup
12. neck
13. cast
14. Children will write *n* and they will circle the nut and the notebook.
15. Children will write *n* and they will circle the nail and the nurse.
16. Children will write *n* and they will circle the moon and the lion.
17. Children will write *n* and they will circle the pen and the spoon.
18. Children will write *c* and they will circle the cake and the coat.

19. Children will write *c* and they will circle the corn and the cookie.
20. Children will draw a line to the fruit stand and color the banana yellow.
21. Children will draw a line to the plate of vegetables and color the carrot orange.
22. Children will draw a line to the fruit stand and color the apple red.

Unit 5

Items 1–6:
Children will circle the following:

1. cat
2. boys playing baseball
3. is
4. the girl and the boy feeding the hamster
5. the girl watering the tall plant
6. the bunch of grapes
7. Children will draw a line to the broken vase.

Items 8–15:
Children will circle the following:

8. is
9. play
10. flower
11. feet
12. pot
13. fish
14. 3 dots
15. 4 dots
16. Children will circle the word *mop* and write *mop*.
17. Children will circle the word *top* and write *top*.
18. Children will circle the word *fin* and write *fin*.
19. Children will circle the word *fan* and write *fan*.

20. Children will circle the word *pot* and write *pot*.
21. Children will circle the word *fox* and write *fox*.
22. Children will draw a circle around the airplane and the building blocks.
23. Children will draw an *X* over the horse and the squirrel.
24. Children will draw a circle around the bird and the butterfly.

Unit 6

1. b
2. b
3. b
4. a
5. c
6. a
7. c
8. a
9. b
10. c
11. b
12. c
13. b
14. b
15. b
16. c
17. c
18. b
19. a
20. c
21. a
22. a
23. b
24. b
25. c
26. a

Unit 7

1. a
2. c
3. b
4. b
5. c
6. b
7. b
8. c
9. a
10. b
11. c
12. c
13. a
14. b
15. c
16. c
17. c
18. b
19. b
20. a
21. c
22. a
23. a
24. b
25. c
26. b
27. a

Unit 8

1. a
2. c
3. b
4. c
5. b
6. c
7. a
8. c
9. c
10. b
11. a
12. b
13. a
14. a
15. c
16. c
17. a
18. c
19. b
20. b
21. c
22. c
23. a
24. b
25. c
26. c
27. b

Unit 9

1. c
2. a
3. b
4. b
5. a
6. a
7. c
8. a
9. c
10. b
11. c
12. a
13. b
14. b
15. a
16. b
17. c
18. c
19. a
20. c
21. b
22. a
23. a
24. a
25. c
26. a
27. b

Unit 10

1. c
2. b
3. b
4. b
5. c
6. a
7. c
8. c
9. b
10. a
11. b
12. c
13. a
14. a
15. b
16. a
17. b
18. c
19. c
20. a
21. b
22. b
23. c
24. a

Answer Key Benchmark Assessments

Benchmark Test A

Items 1–3:
Children will circle the following:

1. boy
2. children playing in pool
3. Dad cutting cake
4. Children will a draw a line to the children sledding down the hill.
5. Children will draw a line to the melted popsicle.
6. Children will circle the boy reading.
7. Children will circle the kitten playing with string and draw a line under the kitten talking on the phone.
8. Children will draw an X through the bird.
9. Children will make a check under the lunch bag with raisins and an X under the lunch bag that does not have raisins.

Items 10–17:
Children will circle the following:

10. we
11. like
12. see
13. go
14. here
15. was
16. my
17. with
18. Children will write *s*.
19. Children will write *p*.
20. Children will write *d*.
21. Children will circle the pig and bag and they will write *g*.
22. Children will circle the can and pin and they will write *n*.
23. Children will circle the pot and bat and they will write *t*.
24. Children will circle *tub* and they will write *tub*.
25. Children will circle *six* and they will write *six*.
26. Children will circle *box* and they will write *box*.
27. Children will circle *can* and they will write *can*.
28. Children will circle *jet* and they will write *jet*.

Benchmark Test B

Items 1–3:
Children will circle the following:

1. ballet slipper
2. dog sitting with a ballet shoe in his mouth
3. girl at ballet class
4. Children will draw a line to the boy walking his dog at the park.
5. Children will draw a line to the puddle that turned to ice.
6. Children will circle the girl eating cereal.
7. Children will circle the boy playing with the action figure and draw a line under the boy flying through the air.
8. Children will draw an X through the butterfly.
9. Children will make a check under the first group of items and an X under the second group of items.

Items 10–17:
Children will circle the following:

10. look
11. me
12. where
13. she
14. to
15. and
16. play
17. for
18. Children will write *s*.
19. Children will write *p*.
20. Children will write *d*.
21. Children will circle the leg and wig and they will write *g*.
22. Children will circle the numeral ten (10) and bun and they will write *n*.
23. Children will circle the net and bat and they will write *t*.
24. Children will circle *rug* and they will write *rug*.
25. Children will circle *lip* and they will write *lip*.
26. Children will circle *hop* and they will write *hop*.
27. Children will circle *map* and they will write *map*.
28. Children will circle *bed* and they will write *bed*.

Teacher's Notes

Unit and Benchmark Assessment • Grade K

The Print Awareness Assessment and Evaluation Form

The Print Awareness Assessment and the Evaluation Form offer two additional methods for assessing children's progress. They may be used at any time during the school year. Multiple observations may be needed until the desired level of behavior is exhibited.

The Print Awareness Assessment is designed to be administered on an individual basis. It is important to determine what a student already knows about books, print, and the reading process before reading instruction begins.

The Evaluation Form allows you to evaluate a child's social skills, attitudes, and behavior, as well as their understanding of concepts of print. It is designed to be used at various points throughout the school year. You may wish to observe children early in the year, midyear, and at the end of the year to note their progress. This form can also be helpful when preparing for parent conferences. It is designed to inform instruction rather than to determine an individual student's placement.

Keep in mind the following as you administer the assessment:

- Be flexible and base decisions on your knowledge of your students.

- It is not necessary to administer the Print Awareness Assessment to a student if you have already observed that particular behavior.

- Be sensitive to students' language, linguistic, and cultural differences.

Print Awareness Assessment

The Print Awareness Assessment can aid in determining a child's readiness to read. It is simple and quick to administer, and can be done at any time in the school year.

To administer this assessment, select a storybook with illustrations at the top of the page and several lines of text at the bottom of the page. Turn to the first page of the story and read all the questions below to the child.

Directions

Say: *We are going to talk about how to read a story. I will ask you some questions. You will point to something in the book to answer each question.*

If I am going to read this story, where do I begin to read? Point to the place where I start reading. (Child should point to the first word on the page.)

Show me a sentence. Point to where the sentence begins and ends. (Child should identify a sentence's beginning and ending, indicating left-to-right progression.)

Show me one word. What comes before and after the word? (Child should point to a word and explain that a space comes before and after each word.)

Show me a lowercase letter. Put your finger on it. (Child should put his or her finger on a lowercase letter.)

Show me an uppercase letter. Put your finger on it. (Child should put his or her finger on an uppercase letter.)

Determine the number of questions answered correctly out of the five questions.

Name _____ Date _____

Evaluation Form

SCORING
① Needs to Improve ② Fair ③ Good ④ Excellent

Dates of observations:			
Social Skills			
Appreciates and values other points of view			
Develops an awareness of the classroom as a community of learners that values cooperation, fair play, and respect for all			
Develops and expresses personal interests and attitudes			
Cooperates with others			
Appreciates and values diverse points of view			
Becomes aware of cultural backgrounds, experiences, emotions, and ideas of self			
Works together with others			
Responds to others in a variety of ways			
Concepts of Print			
Demonstrates awareness of concepts of print: directionality, letters, words sentences, punctuation, illustrations			
Comments:			

Unit 1 Reteaching and Intervention Opportunities

TESTED SKILLS AND STRATEGIES	Teacher's Edition		Additional Lessons	Practice Book	Activity Book	Intervention Teacher's Guide	ELL Teacher's Guide
	Small Group						
Comprehension Skills							
Identify Setting, 1, 6, 7	151-152, 158-159		T5	28	15-16, 21	See Guide	24
Make Predictions, 2, 4, 5	75-76, 82-83, 227-228, 234-235		T4	22, 34	5-6, 11, 25, 31	See Guide	12, 36
High-Frequency Words							
the, 3, 8	142, 150, 155-156, 218, 226, 231-232		T6	29-30, 35-36	17-18, 27-28	See Guide	10, 34
we, 9	66, 74, 79-80, 218, 226, 231-232		T6	23-24, 35-36	7-8, 27-28	See Guide	22, 34
Phonemic Awareness							
Onset and Rime Blending, 10, 11			T1			See Guide	
Phoneme Isolation, 12	66, 68, 74, 78, 142, 144, 146, 150, 218, 220, 222, 226		T1	25, 31	9, 19	See Guide	
Phoneme Blending, 13	146, 154, 230		T1		20, 30	See Guide	
Phonics							
*/m/*m, 14, 15, 16	67, 70, 75-76, 80, 82, 219-220, 222, 227, 230, 234		T2	21, 26, 33, 39-40	4, 10, 24, 32	See Guide	8-9, 32-33
*Short /a/*a, 17, 18, 19	143-144, 146, 151-152, 154, 158, 219, 222, 228, 230, 234, 337		T3	27, 32, 37, 39-40	14, 22, 29, 32	See Guide	20-21, 32-33
Concept Words							
Size words: big/small, short/tall, 20, 21, 22, 23			T7		26	See Guide	

Unit 2 Reteaching and Intervention Opportunities

TESTED SKILLS AND STRATEGIES	Teacher's Edition		Additional Lessons	Practice Book	Activity Book	Intervention Teacher's Guide	ELL Teacher's Guide
	Small Group						
Comprehension Skills							
Identify Character, 1, 4, 5	319-320, 326-327, 471-472, 478-479		T4	42, 54	5-6, 11, 25-26, 31	See Guide	54
Compare and Contrast, 3, 6, 7	395-396, 402-403		T5	48	15, 21	See Guide	66
High-Frequency Words							
a, 2, 8	386, 394, 399-400, 462, 470, 475-476		T6	49-50, 55-56	17-18, 27-28	See Guide	64
like, 9	310, 318, 323-324, 462, 470, 475-476		T6	43-44, 55-56	7-8, 27-28	See Guide	52
Phonemic Awareness							
Phoneme Isolation, 10, 11	310, 312, 314, 318, 386, 388, 390, 394, 462, 464, 466		T1	45, 51	9, 19	See Guide	
Phoneme Blending, 12, 13	314, 322, 390, 398, 466, 470, 474, 478		T1		10, 20, 30	See Guide	
Phonics							
Initial /s/s, 14, 15	311-312, 314, 319-320, 322, 326, 463-464, 466, 471-472, 474, 478		T2	41, 46, 53, 57-60	4, 12, 24, 32	See Guide	50-51, 74-75
/p/p, 16, 17	307 300, 390, 395-390, 402, 463-464, 466, 471-472, 474, 478		T3	47, 52-53, 57-60	14, 22, 29, 32	See Guide	62-63 74-75
/m/m, 18						See Guide	
Short /a/a, 19						See Guide	
Concept Words							
Color Words: Red, Yellow, Blue, 20, 21, 22			T7		16	See Guide	

Unit 3 Reteaching and Intervention Opportunities

| TESTED SKILLS AND STRATEGIES | Teacher's Edition | | Practice Book | Activity Book | Intervention Guide | ELL Teacher's Guide |
	Small Group	Additional Lessons				
Comprehension Skills						
Classify and Categorize, 1, 7	639-640, 646-647	T4	68	15-16, 21	See Guide	108
Identify Character, Plot, 2, 4, 5	715-716, 722-723	T5	74	25-26, 31	See Guide	120
Make and Confirm Predictions, 6	563-564, 570-571	T4	62	5, 11	See Guide	96
High-Frequency Words						
see, 8	554, 562, 567-568, 706, 714, 719-720	T6	63-64, 75-76	7-8, 27-28	See Guide	94, 118
go, 3, 9	630, 638, 643-644, 706, 714, 719-720	T6	69-70, 75-76	17-18, 27-28	See Guide	106, 118
Phonemic Awareness						
Phoneme Isolation, 10, 11	554, 556, 558, 562, 630, 632, 634, 638, 706, 708, 710	T1	65, 71	9, 19	See Guide	
Phoneme Blending, 12, 13	558, 566, 634, 642, 710, 714, 718	T1		10, 20, 30	See Guide	
Phonics						
/t/t, 14, 15, 16	555-556, 558, 563-564, 566, 570, 707-708, 710, 715-716, 718, 722	T2	61, 66, 73, 77-80	4, 12, 24, 32	See Guide	92-93, 116-117
Short /i/i, 17, 18, 19	631-632, 634, 639-640, 642, 646, 707-708, 710, 715-716, 718, 722	T3	67, 72-73, 77-80	14, 22, 29, 32	See Guide	104-105, 116-117
Concept Words						
Shape Words: Square, Circle, Triangle, 20, 21, 22		T7		6	See Guide	

Unit 4 Reteaching and Intervention Opportunities

TESTED SKILLS AND STRATEGIES	Teacher's Edition		Practice Book	Activity Book	Intervention Guide	ELL Teacher's Guide
	Small Group	Additional Lessons				
Comprehension Skills						
Identify Sequence of Events, 1, 4, 5	805-806, 812-813	T4	82	5-6, 11	See Guide	138
Make Inferences, 3, 6, 7	881-882, 888-889, 957-958, 964-965	T5	88, 94	15-16, 21, 25, 31	See Guide	150, 162
High-Frequency Words						
to, 2, 8	796, 804, 809-810, 948, 956, 961-962	T6	83-84, 95-96	7-8, 27-28	See Guide	136, 160
have, 9	872, 880, 885-886, 948, 956, 961-962	T6	89-90, 95-96	17-18, 27-28	See Guide	148, 160
Phonemic Awareness						
Phoneme Isolation, 10, 11	796, 798, 800, 804, 872, 874, 876, 880, 948, 950, 952	T1	85, 91	9, 19, 29	See Guide	
Phoneme Blending, 12, 13	800, 808, 876, 884, 949, 952, 956, 960	T1		10, 20, 30	See Guide	
Phonics						
/n/n, 14, 15, 16, 17	797-798, 800, 805-806, 808, 812, 949-950, 952, 957-958, 960, 964	T2	81, 86, 93, 97-100	4, 12, 21, 31	See Guide	176-177, 200-201
Initial /c/c, 18, 19	873-874, 876, 881-882, 884, 888, 949-950, 952, 957-958, 960, 964	T3	87, 92-93, 97-100	14, 22, 32	See Guide	188-189, 200-201
Concept Words						
Fruits and Vegetables: Apple, Carrot, Banana, 20, 21, 22		T7		26	See Guide	

Unit 5 Reteaching and Intervention Opportunities

| TESTED SKILLS AND STRATEGIES | Teacher's Edition | | Practice Book | Activity Book | Intervention Guide | ELL Teacher's Guide |
	Small Group	Additional Lessons				
Comprehension Skills						
Identify Character, Plot, 1, 4, 5	1201-1202, 1208-1209	T5	114	25-26, 31	See Guide	204
Make and Confirm Predictions, 2, 7	1049-1050, 1053-1054	T4	102	5, 11	See Guide	180
Classify and Categorize, 6	1125-1126, 1132-1133	T4	108	15-16, 21	See Guide	192
High-Frequency Words						
is, 3, 8	1040, 1048, 1053-1054, 1192, 1200, 1205-1206	T6	103-104, 115-116	7-8, 27-28	See Guide	178, 202
play, 9	1116, 1124, 1129-1130, 1192, 1200, 1205-1206	T6	109-110, 115-116	17-18, 27-28	See Guide	190, 202
Phonemic Awareness						
Phoneme Isolation, 10, 11	1040, 1042, 1044, 1048, 1116, 1118, 1120, 1124, 1192, 1194, 1196	T1	105, 111	9, 19	See Guide	
Phoneme Blending, 12, 13	1044, 1052, 1120, 1128, 1196, 1204	T1		10, 20, 30	See Guide	
Phoneme Segmentation, 14, 15	1200	T1			See Guide	
Phonics						
Short /o/o, 16, 17, 20	1041-1042, 1044, 1049-1050, 1052, 1056, 1193-1194, 1196, 1201, 1202, 1204, 1208	T2	101, 106, 113, 117-120	4, 12, 24, 32	See Guide	176-177, 200-201
Initial /f/f, 18, 19, 21	1117-1118, 1120, 1125-1126, 1128, 1132, 1193-1194, 1196, 1201-1202, 1204, 1208	T3	107, 112-113, 117-120	14, 22, 29, 32	See Guide	188-189, 200-201
Concept Words						
Position Words: Under, Behind, On, 22, 23, 24		T7		6	See Guide	

Unit 6 Reteaching and Intervention Opportunities

TESTED SKILLS AND STRATEGIES	Teacher's Edition		Practice Book	Activity Book	Intervention Guide	ELL Teacher's Guide
	Small Group	Additional Lessons				
Comprehension Skills						
Identify Main Idea and Details, 1, 4, 5	1291-1292, 1298-1299, 1367-1368, 1374-1375	T6	122, 128	5-6, 11, 15, 21	See Guide	222, 234
Retell, 3, 6, 7	1443-1444, 1450-1451	T7	134	25-26, 31	See Guide	246
High-Frequency Words						
you, 2, 10	1358, 1366, 1371-1372, 1434, 1442, 1447-1448	T8	129-130, 135-136	17-18, 27-28	See Guide	232, 244
are, 8	1282, 1290, 1295-1296, 1434, 1442, 1447-1448	T8	123-124, 135-136	7-8, 27-28	See Guide	220, 244
for, 9	1358, 1366, 1371-1372, 1434, 1442, 1447-1448	T8	129-130, 135-136	17-18, 27-28	See Guide	232, 244
Phonemic Awareness						
Phoneme Isolation, 11, 12	1282, 1284, 1286, 1358, 1360, 1362, 1366, 1434, 1436, 1438	T1	125	9	See Guide	
Phoneme Blending, 13, 14	1286, 1290, 1294, 1362, 1370, 1438, 1442, 1446	T1			See Guide	
Phoneme Segmentation, 15, 16, 17	1442	T1			See Guide	
Phonics						
Initial /h/h, 18	1283-1284, 1286, 1291-1292, 1294, 1298, 1435-1436, 1438, 1443-1444, 1450	T2	121, 125-126, 133, 138-140	4, 10, 12, 24, 30, 32	See Guide	218-219, 242-243
Initial and Final /d/d, 19, 21	1359-1360, 1362, 1435-1436, 1438, 1443-1444, 1450	T3	127, 132, 137-140	14, 20, 22, 29- 30, 32	See Guide	230-231, 242-243
Initial /r/r, 20	1367-1368, 1370, 1374, 1435-1436, 1438, 1443-1444, 1450	T4	131-132, 137-140	19-20, 22, 29- 30, 32	See Guide	230-231, 242-243
Word Families: -at, -an, 22, 23	1446-1447	T5			See Guide	
Concept Words						
Sequence Words: First, Next, Last, 24, 25, 26		T9		16	See Guide	

Unit 7 Reteaching and Intervention Opportunities

TESTED SKILLS AND STRATEGIES	Teacher's Edition		Practice Book	Activity Book	Intervention Guide	ELL Teacher's Guide
	Small Group	Additional Lessons				
Comprehension Skills						
Identify Setting, 1, 6	1611-1612, 1618-1619	T7	148	15-16, 21	See Guide	276
Distinguish Between Fantasy and Reality, 2, 7	1687-1688, 1694-1695	T8	154	25, 31	See Guide	288
Identify Main Idea and Details, 4, 5	1535-1536, 1542-1543	T6	142	5-6, 11	See Guide	264
High-Frequency Words						
this, 3, 8	1526, 1534, 1539-1540, 1678, 1686, 1691-1692	T9	143-144, 155-156	7-8, 27-28	See Guide	262, 286
do, 9	1526, 1534, 1539-1540, 1678, 1686, 1691-1692	T9	143-144, 155-156		See Guide	262, 286
what, 11	1602, 1610, 1615-1616, 1678, 1686, 1691-1692	T9	149-150, 155-156	17-18, 27-28	See Guide	274, 286
and, 10	1602, 1610, 1615-1616, 1678, 1686, 1691-1692	T9	149-150, 155-156	17-18, 27-28	See Guide	274, 286
Phonemic Awareness						
Phoneme Isolation, 12, 13	1526, 1528, 1530, 1534, 1602, 1604, 1606, 1610, 1678, 1680, 1682	T1	145	9	See Guide	
Phoneme Blending, 14, 15	1530, 1538, 1606, 1614, 1682, 1690	T1			See Guide	
Phoneme Segmentation, 16, 17, 18	1686	T1			See Guide	
Phonics						
Initial /e/e, 16	1527-1528, 1530, 1535, 1538, 1542, 1679-1680, 1682, 1687-1688, 1690, 1694	T2	141, 146, 153, 157-160	4, 10, 12, 20, 24, 30, 32	See Guide	260-261, 284-285
Initial and Final /b/b, 17, 19	1603-1604, 1606, 1679-1680, 1682, 1687-1688, 1690, 1694	T3	147, 152, 157-160	14, 20, 22, 29-30, 32	See Guide	272-273, 284-285
Initial /l/l, 18	1611-1612, 1614, 1618, 1679-1680, 1682, 1687-1688, 1690, 1694	T4	151-152, 157-160	19-20, 22, 29-30, 32	See Guide	272-273, 284-285
Word Families: -it, -ip, 20, 21		T5			See Guide	
Concept Words						
Words that Compare: Tallest, Smallest, Longest, 22, 23, 24		T11		26	See Guide	

© Macmillan/McGraw-Hill

Unit 8 Reteaching and Intervention Opportunities

| TESTED SKILLS AND STRATEGIES | Teacher's Edition | | Practice Book | Activity Book | Intervention Guide | ELL Teacher's Guide |
	Small Group	Additional Lessons				
Comprehension Skills						
Identify Sequence of Events, 1, 4, 5	1773-1774, 1781-1782	T5	162	5-6, 11	See Guide	306
Draw Conclusions, 3, 6	1929-1930, 1936-1937	T7	174	25, 31	See Guide	330
Retell, 7	1853-1854, 1860-1861	T6	168	15-16, 21	See Guide	318
High-Frequency Words						
little, 2, 8	1768, 1772, 1777-1778, 1920, 1928, 1933-1934	T8	163-164, 175-176	7-8, 27-28	See Guide	304, 328
said, 9	1768, 1772, 1777-1778, 1920, 1928, 1933-1934	T8	163-164, 175-176	7-8, 27-28	See Guide	304, 328
here, 10	1844, 1852, 1857-1858, 1920, 1928, 1933-1934	T8	169-170, 175-176	17-18, 27-28	See Guide	316, 328
was, 11		T8	169-170, 175-176	17-18, 27-28	See Guide	316, 328
Phonemic Awareness						
Phoneme Isolation, 12, 13	1768, 1770, 1772, 1776, 1844, 1846, 1848, 1852, 1920, 1922, 1924	T1	165, 171	9, 19	See Guide	
Phoneme Blending, 14, 15	1772, 1780, 1848, 1856, 1932	T1			See Guide	
Phoneme Segmentation, 16, 17, 18	1924	T1			See Guide	
Phonics						
Initial /k/k and Final /k/ck, 19, 20	1769-1770, 1772, 1777, 1780, 1784, 1921-1922, 1924, 1929- 1930, 1932, 1936	T2	161, 165, 173, 178, 179-180	4, 10, 12, 24, 30, 32	See Guide	302-303, 326-327
Short /u/u, 21	1845-1846, 1848, 1853-1854, 1856, 1860, 1921-1922, 1924, 1929-1930, 1932, 1936	T3	167, 172, 177-180	14, 20, 22, 29-30, 32	See Guide	314-315, 326-327
Word Families: -ot, -op, -ick, 22, 23, 24		T4			See Guide	
Concept Words						
Position Words: Top, Middle, Bottom, 25, 26, 27		T9		26	See Guide	

Unit 9 Reteaching and Intervention Opportunities

| TESTED SKILLS AND STRATEGIES | Teacher's Edition | | Practice Book | Activity Book | Intervention Guide | ELL Teacher's Guide |
	Small Group	Additional Lessons				
Comprehension Skills						
Distinguish Between Fantasy and Reality, 1, 6	2173-2174, 2180-2181	T7	194	25, 31	See Guide	372
Compare and Contrast, 2, 4, 5	2097-2098, 2104-2105	T6	188	15-16, 21	See Guide	360
Classify and Categorize, 7	2021-2022, 2028-2029	T5	182	5-6, 11	See Guide	348
High-Frequency Words						
she, 3, 8	2012, 2020, 2025-2026, 2164, 2172, 2177-2178	T8	183-184, 194-195	7-8, 27-28	See Guide	346, 370
he, 9	2012, 2020, 2025-2026, 2164, 2172, 2177-2178	T8	183-184, 194-195	7-8, 27-28	See Guide	346, 370
has, 10	2088, 2096, 2101-2102, 2164, 2172, 2177-2178	T8	189-190, 194-195	17-18, 27-28	See Guide	358, 370
look, 11		T8	189-190, 194-195	17-18, 27-28	See Guide	358, 370
Phonemic Awareness						
Phoneme Isolation, 12, 13	2012, 2014, 2016, 2020, 2088, 2090, 2092, 2097-2098, 2100, 2104, 2164, 2166, 2168	T1		9	See Guide	
Phoneme Blending, 14, 15	2016, 2024, 2092, 2100	T1			See Guide	
Phoneme Segmentation, 16, 17, 18	2176	T1				
Phonics						
Initial /w/w, 19	2021-2022, 2024, 2028, 2165-2166, 2168, 2173-2174, 2176, 2180	T2	185-186, 193	10, 12, 24, 30, 32	See Guide	344-345, 368-369
Initial /v/v, 20	2097-2098, 2100, 2104, 2165-2166, 2168, 2173-2174, 2176, 2180	T3	191-192, 197-200	19-20, 22, 29-30, 32	See Guide	344-345, 368-369
Final /g/g, 21	2013-2014, 2016, 2165-2166, 2168, 2173-2174, 2176, 2180	T2	181, 186, 193, 198-200	4, 10, 12, 24, 30, 32	See Guide	356-357, 368-369
Final /ks/x, 22	2089-2090, 2092, 2165-2166, 2168, 2173-2174, 2176, 2180	T3	187, 192, 197-200	14, 20, 22, 29-30, 32	See Guide	356-357, 368-369
Concept Words						
Opposites: big/small, short/tall, thin/fat, 23, 24, 25		T9		26	See Guide	

© Macmillan/McGraw-Hill

Unit 10 Reteaching and Intervention Opportunities

TESTED SKILLS AND STRATEGIES	Teacher's Edition		Practice Book	Activity Book	Intervention Guide	ELL Teacher's Guide
	Small Group	Additional Lessons				
Comprehension Skills						
Use Illustrations, 1, 4, 5	2263-2264, 2270-2271	T6	202	5-6, 11	See Guide	
Identify Cause and Effect, 2, 6	2339-2340, 2346-2347	T7	208	15-16, 21	See Guide	
Identify Setting, 7	2415-2416, 2422-2423	T8	214	25, 31	See Guide	
High-Frequency Words						
with, 8	2254, 2262, 2267-2268, 2406, 2414, 2419-2420	T9	203-204, 215-216	7-8, 27-28	See Guide	
my, 3, 9	2254, 2262, 2267-2268, 2406, 2414, 2419-2420	T9	203-204, 215-216	7-8, 27-28	See Guide	
me, 10	2330, 2338, 2343-2344, 2406, 2414, 2419-2420	T9	209-210, 215-216	17-18, 27-28	See Guide	
where, 11	2330, 2338, 2343-2344, 2406, 2414, 2419-2420	T9	209-210, 215-216	17-18, 27-28	See Guide	
Phonemic Awareness						
Phoneme Isolation, 12, 13	2254, 2256, 2258, 2330, 2332, 2334, 2338, 2406, 2408, 2410	T1			See Guide	
Phoneme Blending, 14, 15	2258, 2266, 2334, 2342, 2410, 2414, 2418	T1			See Guide	
Phonics						
Initial /j/j, 16	2255-2256, 2258, 2407-2408, 2410, 2415-2416, 2418, 2422	T3	201, 206, 213, 218-220	4, 10, 12, 24, 30, 32	See Guide	386-387
Initial /y/y, 17	2331-2332, 2334, 2407-2408, 2410, 2415-2416, 2418, 2422	T4	207, 212, 217-220	14, 20, 22, 29-30, 32	See Guide	398-399
Initial /z/z, 18	2339-2340, 2342, 2346, 2407-2408, 2410, 2415-2416, 2418, 2422	T4	211-212, 217-220	19-20, 22, 29-30, 32	See Guide	398-399
Initial /kw/qu, 19	2263-2264, 2266, 2407-2408, 2410, 2415-2416, 2418, 2422, 2470	T3	205-206, 213, 218-220	9-10, 12, 24, 30, 32	See Guide	386-387
Word families -ut, -un, 20, 21		T5			See Guide	
Concept Words						
Number Words: two, four, five, 22, 23, 24		T10		26	See Guide	

© Macmillan/McGraw-Hill

Teacher's Notes

Unit and Benchmark Assessment • Grade K